MULTILEVEL ACTIVITY BOOK
FOUNDATIONS
Second Edition

Steven J. Molinsky • Bill Bliss

PEARSON
Longman

Foundations Multilevel Activity Book, second edition

Pearson Education, 10 Bank Street, White Plains, NY 10606

Editorial director: *Pam Fishman*
Vice president, director of design and production: *Rhea Banker*
Director of electronic production: *Aliza Greenblatt*
Director of manufacturing: *Patrice Fraccio*
Senior manufacturing manager: *Edith Pullman*
Director of marketing: *Oliva Fernandez*
Production editor: *Diane Cipollone*
Senior digital layout specialist: *Lisa Ghiozzi*
Text design: *Wendy Wolf*
Text composition: *TSI Graphics*
Cover design: *Warren Fischbach; Wendy Wolf; Wanda España,
 Wee Design Group*
Realia creation: *Lisa Ghiozzi; Warren Fischbach; Wendy Wolf*
Illustrations: *Richard E. Hill*

ISBN 0-13-135437-X; 978-0-13-135437-1

Longman on the Web
Longman.com offers online resources for teachers
and students.
Access our Companion Websites, our online catalog,
and our local offices around the world.
Visit us at longman.com.

Printed in the United States of America
 5 6 7 8 9 10 – VOLL – 12 11

Contents

For user convenience, pages are labeled and numbered within their respective sections.

FOUNDATIONS MULTILEVEL ACTIVITIES: SCOPE & SEQUENCE

LITERACY, READING, & NUMERACY CURRICULUM

UNIT	LITERACY	EVIDENCE-BASED READING	NUMERACY	CURRICULUM STANDARDS		
				CASAS	LAUSD	FLORIDA
Pre-unit	• Left-to-right & top-to-bottom progression • Identify similar & different shapes, sizes, directionality, signs, & letters • Hold writing utensil appropriately • Recognize, trace, & copy upper & lower case manuscript letters	• Phonemic awareness: Phoneme isolation, identification, categorization, blending, & segmentation	• Recognize, trace, & copy numbers	R1.1, R1.3, R1.4, R2.2, R4.1	15, 16, 17, 21, 22, 23, 26	01.01, 01.02, 01.03, 01.04, 01.05, 01.06, 01.07, 01.08, 01.11, 07.02
1	• Recognize pictures & words • Recognize, trace, & copy upper & lower case manuscript letters • Differentiate between upper and lower case manuscript letters • Trace & copy words with manuscript letters	• Decoding: Consonants + Short Vowels + Consonants • Concepts of print: letters, words, sentences • Fluency	• Recognize, trace, & copy numbers 0–10	R1.1–R1.6, R2.2, R3.1, R3.2, R4.1	16, 17, 19, 21, 22, 23, 24, 26	01.04, 01.05, 01.06, 01.07, 01.10, 07.06, 07.08, 01.11, 15.04
2	• Recognize pictures & words • Trace & copy words with manuscript letters	• Decoding: Short & long vowels • Concepts of print • Fluency	• Recognize, trace, & copy numbers 11–19	R1.1–R1.6, R2.2, R3.1, R4.1	17, 19, 21, 23, 24, 26	01.04, 07.06, 07.08, 07.12, 15.04
3	• Recognize pictures & words • Trace & copy words with manuscript letters	• Decoding: Short & long vowels • Concepts of print • Fluency	• Recognize, trace, & copy numbers 20–100	R1.1–R1.6, R2.2, R3.1, R4.1	17, 19, 21, 23, 24, 26	07.03, 07.06, 07.08, 07.12, 15.04
4	• Recognize pictures & words • Recognize abbreviations for days of week & months of year • Trace & copy words with manuscript letters	• Decoding: Short & long vowels • Concepts of print • Fluency	• Time • Money	R1.1–R1.6, R2.2, R2.6, R3.1, R4.1, R4.2, R4.4	17, 19, 21, 22, 23, 24, 26	07.03, 07.06, 07.08, 07.12, 15.04
5	• Recognize pictures & words • Trace & copy words with manuscript letters	• Decoding: Long vowel word families • Concepts of print • Fluency	• Ordinal Numbers	R1.1–R1.6, R2.2, R3.1, R4.1	17, 19, 21, 22, 23, 24, 26	07.03, 07.06, 07.08, 07.12, 15.01, 15.04
6	• Recognize pictures & words • Trace & copy words with manuscript letters	• Decoding: Initial & final consonant blends • Concepts of print • Fluency	• Counting items	R1.1–R1.6, R2.2, R3.1, R4.1	17, 19, 21, 22, 23, 24, 26	07.03, 07.06, 07.08, 07.12, 15.04
7	• Recognize pictures & words • Recognize words with opposite meanings • Trace & copy words with manuscript letters	• Decoding: Initial consonant blends; y as a vowel • Concepts of print • Fluency	• Numbers indicating height, weight, & age	R1.1–R1.6, R2.2, R3.1, R4.1	17, 19, 21, 22, 23, 24, 26	07.03, 07.06, 07.08, 07.12, 15.02, 15.04

CASAS: Comprehensive Adult Student Assessment System, Generic Reading Basic Skills Content Standards—Level A
LAUSD: Los Angeles Unified School District, ESL Beginning Literacy Written Language Skills Proficiencies
FLORIDA: Literacy for Adult ESOL Learners Objectives (LCP-A, B, C)

LITERACY, READING, & NUMERACY CURRICULUM

UNIT	LITERACY	EVIDENCE-BASED READING	NUMERACY	CURRICULUM STANDARDS		
				CASAS	LAUSD	FLORIDA
8	• Recognize pictures & words • Trace & copy words with manuscript letters	• Decoding: Initial & final consonant digraphs; Two-syllable words with final /e	• Units of measure	R1.1–R1.6, R2.2, R3.1, R4.1	17, 19, 21, 22, 23, 24, 26	07.03, 07.06, 07.08, 07.12, 15.04, 15.07
9	• Recognize pictures & words • Trace & copy words with manuscript letters	• Concepts of print • Fluency • Organize words into categories		R1.1–R1.6, R2.2, R3.1, R4.1, R4.4	17, 19, 21, 22, 23, 24, 26	07.03, 07.06, 07.08, 07.11, 15.04, 15.07
10	• Recognize pictures & words • Trace & copy words with manuscript letters	• Decoding: Vowel digraphs • Concepts of print • Fluency • Organize words into categories	• Dollar amounts	R1.1–R1.6, R2.2, R3.1, R4.1, R4.4	17, 19, 21, 22, 23, 24, 26	07.03, 07.06, 07.08, 07.12, 15.04
11	• Recognize pictures & words • Recognize, trace, & copy upper case & lower case cursive letters • Recognize difference between manuscript & cursive writing	• Decoding: R-controlled vowels; Vowel Diphthongs • Concepts of print • Fluency	• Writing a check	R1.1–R1.6, R2.2, R3.1, R4.1, R4.4	17, 19, 21, 22, 23, 24, 26	07.03, 07.07, 07.08, 07.12, 15.03, 15.04
12	• Recognize pictures & words • Trace & copy words with cursive letters	• Decoding: Vowel sounds & spelling patterns • Concepts of print • Fluency	• Medicine label instructions	R1.1–R1.6, R2.2, R3.1, R4.1	17, 19, 21, 22, 23, 24, 26, 29	07.03, 07.08, 07.12, 15.01, 15.03, 15.04
13	• Recognize pictures & words • Trace & copy words with cursive letters	• Decoding: Consonant s = z • Fluency • Organize words into categories	• Class schedule	R1.1–R1.6, R2.2, R3.1, R4.1, R4.2	17, 19, 21, 22, 23, 24, 26, 29	07.03, 07.08, 07.12, 15.03, 15.04, 15.07
14	• Recognize pictures & words • Trace & copy words with cursive letters	• Decoding: Compound words • Concepts of print • Fluency	• Paycheck & pay stub	R1.1–R1.6, R2.2, R3.1, R4.1, R4.4	17, 19, 21, 22, 23, 24, 26, 29	07.08, 07.12, 15.03, 15.04, 15.07
15	• Recognize pictures & words • Trace & copy words with cursive letters	• Rhyming words (same spelling) • Concepts of print • Fluency • Organize words into categories	• Bus schedule	R1.1–R1.6, R2.1, R2.2, R3.1, R4.1, R4.2	17, 18, 19, 21, 22, 23	01.09, 07.03, 07.08, 07.09, 07.12, 15.03, 15.07, 15.09
		• Rhyming words (different spelling) • Concepts of print • Fluency • Organize words into categories	• Dates	R1.1–R1.6, R2.2, R3.1, R4.1, R4.3	17, 19, 21, 22, 23, 24, 26	01.09, 07.03, 07.08, 07.09, 07.12, 15.03, 15.04, 15.07, 15.09

CASAS: Comprehensive Adult Student Assessment System, Generic Reading Basic Skills Content Standards—Level A
LAUSD: Los Angeles Unified School District, ESL Beginning Literacy Written Language Skills Proficiencies
FLORIDA: Literacy for Adult ESOL Learners Objectives (LCP-A, B, C)

Welcome to the *Foundations* Multilevel Activity Book! This volume provides a wealth of reproducible resources for use with the *Foundations* program: assessment tools; evidence-based reading activities; supplemental worksheets for preliteracy, literacy, handwriting, number, and vocabulary practice; classroom labels; flash cards; and activity masters to accompany the activity suggestions contained in the *Foundations* Teacher's Guide.

These materials are also available on the CD-ROM included with the Teacher's Guide. They are provided in this separate volume for the convenience of programs that prefer to have quick access to these materials in printed form rather than as computer files. The materials may be reproduced for classroom use only in conjunction with the *Foundations* instructional program.

ASSESSMENT TOOLS

A **Needs Assessment** questionnaire in an easy pictorial format enables students to indicate their needs and interests to guide the teacher's lesson planning.

A **Performance-Based Lesson Assessment** form is a tool for evaluating and documenting student participation and performance with a simple scoring rubric. Many instructors like to make multiple copies of the form with the names of students filled in so that they have a convenient supply of lesson assessment forms for each class. (The CD-ROM version of this form contains text fields that enable instructors to enter student names prior to printing the form.)

A **Learner Progress Chart** enables students to record their test scores and chart their progress. You may want to keep the charts in a folder and have students update them as each *Foundations* test is completed.

EVIDENCE-BASED READING INSTRUCTION

Phonemic Awareness activities are designed to provide students with systematic, explicit instruction in how to detect the individual speech sounds that make up words. Activities include phoneme isolation, phoneme identification, phoneme categorization, phoneme blending, and phoneme segmentation. These are mostly picture-based listening and speaking activities because their focus is on developing students' sound-recognition skills as a foundation for later or simultaneous instruction in *decoding*—the basic reading process of making connections between printed letters and the sounds they represent. This instruction is particularly important for students who are not literate in their native language. It is also valuable for students who have literacy skills in a non-alphabetic language with a writing system that doesn't involve sound/letter correspondence. Since this form of systematic instruction may be unfamiliar to many teachers, the Phonemic Awareness section of this volume includes step-by-step teaching strategies for these activities.

Basic Reading Practice activities for each unit provide students with systematic, explicit instruction in three fundamental reading skills:

- **Decoding:** the basic reading process of making connections between printed letters and the sounds they represent;

- **Concepts Of Print (Letters, Words, Sentences):** the basic concepts that letters make up words, words make up sentences, and spaces serve to separate these words;

- **Fluency:** the ability to read phrases and sentences aloud correctly with phrasing and expression that is appropriate for the meaning of the text and that demonstrates comprehension.

Through these phonics-based activities, students practice fundamental concepts and skills including short and long vowels, consonant blends, consonant digraphs, vowel digraphs, vowel diphthongs, and rhyming words.

You can use these activities in a variety of ways depending on your students' needs, your class size and schedule, and whether there are tutors, aides, or other people available to work with students in small groups, pairs, or individually. All the activities are suitable for individualized or small-group instruction with a tutor, an aide, or a more skilled student (using cross-ability grouping). The helping person can read a word or a line and have the student repeat. Or the student can try reading the word or line first, then listen to the helping person read it, and then repeat. If pairs of similar-ability students are working together, they can take turns reading and correcting each other. Specific instructions for these activities are provided in the Basic Reading Practice section.

WORKSHEETS

Preliteracy Practice worksheets are designed for students who do not have basic literacy skills in any language. The worksheets provide a careful sequence of instruction that develops basic preliteracy concepts and skills. Students first practice identifying same and different items based on their shapes, their sizes, and their directionality. Then they practice identifying same and different upper case and lower case letters. Pre-Writing worksheets offer practice with the basic elements of letter formation, and Basic Writing worksheets provide tracing and copying practice with upper case letters, lower case letters, and numbers.

Literacy Practice worksheets are mostly picture-word recognition activities in simple matching and multiple-choice formats. The worksheets provide students with basic literacy practice and preparation for the types of questions found on standards-based tests at the beginning literacy level. Two multiple-choice formats of varying difficulty are included in each unit. In the easier format, students see a word and four pictures and they select the correct picture to match the word. In the more challenging format, students see a picture and they select the correct one of four words or expressions to match the picture. Units 1 and 11 Worksheets also include practice with recognition of upper case and lower case letters in both manuscript and cursive forms.

Handwriting Practice worksheets help learners master manuscript and cursive letter formation through tracing and copying activities with key vocabulary in each unit. In addition, the Unit 1 Worksheets offer practice with upper case and lower case manuscript letters, and the Unit 11 Worksheets offer practice with upper case and lower case cursive letters. Students make the transition from manuscript to cursive letters at Unit 11, thereby providing them with ample practice with the cursive form in the final five units of the program. Students should have some basic preliteracy concepts and skills before using these worksheets. (For students who do not yet have these skills, the Foundations Preliteracy Practice Worksheets offer appropriate preparatory practice.)

Number Practice worksheets develop students' numeracy skills through carefully-sequenced practice coordinated with the content of each *Foundations* unit. The initial worksheets provide basic practice in recognizing, tracing, and copying numerals and the words representing numbers, while later worksheets offer life-skills-oriented practice with time, money, and other applications of number skills to everyday life situations.

Vocabulary Practice worksheets review key unit vocabulary through a variety of exercise formats including word choice, sentence completion, and cloze reading. Students also practice common abbreviations and word categorization.

VISUALS

Classroom Labels are large-print signs that can be posted next to key classroom objects and furnishings. While most of the vocabulary relates to Unit 2, it will be useful to have these signs posted in the classroom from the first day of instruction.

Flash Cards provide an economical study tool for students. You can reproduce and cut up each unit's cards to offer students their own set of flash cards for individual practice as well as for classroom activities and games. The flash cards are especially useful for playing Lotto and other matching games in conjunction with the *Foundations* Vocabulary Photo Cards.

ACTIVITY MASTERS

Activity Masters include ready-to-use word cards and activity sheets for the multilevel activities and games suggested throughout the *Foundations* Teacher's Guide.

In conclusion, the *Foundations* Multilevel Activity Book aims to provide you with comprehensive resources for student assessment, multilevel literacy skills development, evidence-based reading instruction, supplemental practice, and dynamic classroom learning through activities and games. We hope that these reproducible materials help you with your lesson-planning and enable you to offer your beginning-literacy and low-beginning learners an instructional program that is effective . . . responsive to students' differing ability levels and learning styles . . . and fun!

Steven J. Molinsky
Bill Bliss

Student's Name _____   I.D. Number _____

Course _____   Teacher _____   Date _____

I want to learn English words for _____.

____ personal information

____ family members

____ the classroom

____ everyday activities

____ leisure activities

____ weather

____ numbers

____ time

____ money

____ days and months

____ rooms and furniture

____ an apartment building

____ places around town

____ describing people

____ describing feelings

____ food

____ supermarket

____ fast food

____ the restaurant

____ colors and clothing

Student's Name _____ I.D. Number _____

I want to learn English words for _____.

____ shopping

____ the bank

____ finances

____ the post office

____ the body

____ ailments and injuries

____ medicine

____ school

____ school subjects

____ school activities

____ occupations

____ job skills

____ job safety

____ transportation

____ places to go

____ sports and recreation

____ entertainment

____ _____

____ _____

____ _____

FOUNDATIONS
Performance-Based Lesson Assessment

Unit / Page(s) _____ Date _____
Class _____ Teacher _____

Student Name	Listening & Speaking	Reading	Writing	Discussion/ Participation
1.				
2.				
3.				
4.				
5.				
6.				
7.				
8.				
9.				
10.				
11.				
12.				
13.				
14.				
15.				
16.				
17.				
18.				
19.				
20.				
21.				
22.				
23.				

Scoring Rubric:

Score the student's performance in each of the following areas: Listening & Speaking, Reading, Writing, and Discussion/Participation.
5 (Excellent), **4** (Good), **3** (Fair), **2** (Poor), **1** (Unsatisfactory)

FOUNDATIONS
Learner Progress Chart

Student's Name _____ I.D. Number _____

Course _____ Teacher _____ Term _____

SCORE

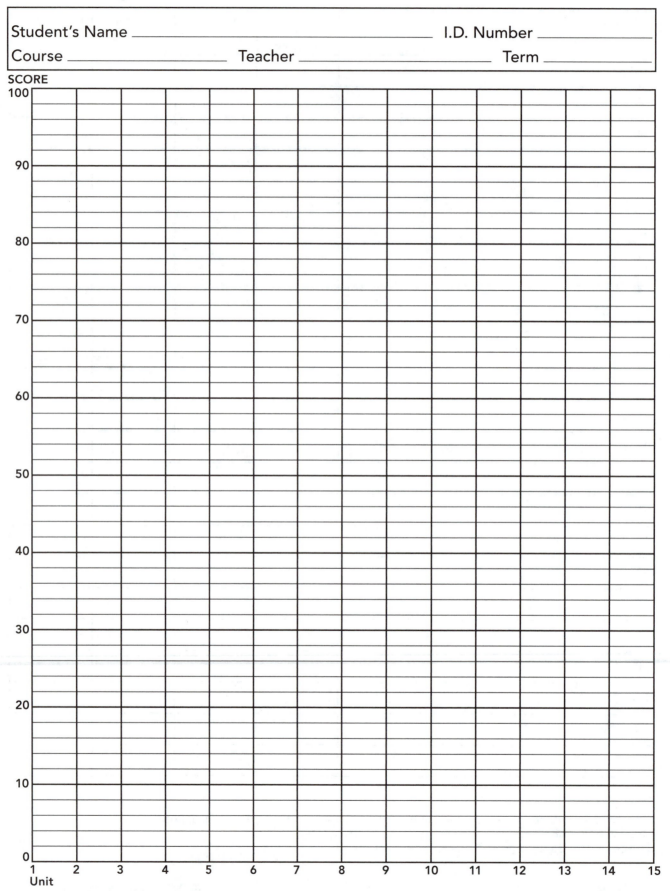

Unit

Foundations
Phonemic Awareness Instructions & Answer Key

Note to Teachers:

The *Foundations* Phonemic Awareness Worksheets are designed to provide students with systematic, explicit instruction in *phonemic awareness*—the ability to detect the individual speech sounds that make up words. This instruction is particularly important for students who are not literate in their native language. It is also valuable for students who have literacy skills in a non-alphabetic language with a writing system that doesn't involve sound/letter correspondence.

The Phonemic Awareness Worksheets are mostly picture-based listening and speaking activities because their focus is on developing students' sound-recognition skills as a foundation for later or simultaneous instruction in *decoding*—the basic reading process of making connections between printed letters and the sounds they represent.

Since these may be among the first worksheets your students use in your instructional program, you can use these activities to introduce or reinforce the basic concept of the top-to-bottom and left-to-right orientation of English text on a page. In Worksheets 1 and 2, each row represents a separate exercise, and the rows are separated by solid lines. In Worksheet 3, each exercise is in a separate box. For Worksheets 1, 2, and 3, it may be helpful to have students use a separate blank sheet of paper to mask all page content below the exercise row or box they are working with. After students complete that exercise, they can move their blank paper down to reveal the next exercise. In Worksheets 4 and 5, there are three exercises in each row. Students can continue to use the separate blank sheet to mask the content below as they become familiar with the "geography" of a typical worksheet in which exercises progress from left to right across the page as well as from top to bottom.

PHONEMIC AWARENESS 1:
Initial Consonant Sounds (with Pictures)

1. **PHONEME ISOLATION** Have students look at the first picture in the top (sample exercise) row. Ask: "What is this?" (A book.) Ask: "What's the first sound in *book*?" (/b/) (Say it as a sound, not the name of the letter "B".) Do the same for the second and fourth words, *board* and *bookshelf*.

2. **PHONEME IDENTIFICATION** Ask: "What sound is the same in *book, board,* and *bookshelf*?" (/b/; the first sound)

3. **PHONEME CATEGORIZATION** Do the following three times as students listen carefully. Say all four words in the top row and ask: "Listen. Which word does not belong? *book, board, ruler, bookshelf.*" (*ruler*) Ask students why the word doesn't belong. (It starts with a different sound.)

4. **MARKING THE ANSWER** Demonstrate how to mark an X on the picture of the ruler in order to show that this word is different from the others. Have students trace over the X on the ruler, and circulate around the classroom to check their work.

5. **EXERCISES 1–5** For the first one or two exercises on the worksheet, do all four steps above in order to assure students are grasping the phonemic awareness concept and developing the required skills. For the rest of the exercises, go immediately to step 3 and have students mark their answers.

6. **PHONEME BLENDING** For additional practice with these pictures, have students listen as you say in sequence the separate sounds that make up one of these words, and have students listen and then say the word. For example: "What word is this? /p/, /e/, /n/" (*pen*) (Reminder: Say the sounds, not the names of the letters.) For an easy version of this activity, tell students the row where the picture of the word is located. For a more challenging version, have students scan the entire worksheet.

Script and Answer Key:
 Ex: book – board – <u>ruler</u> – bookshelf
  1. pen – pencil – penny – <u>desk</u>
  2. TV – <u>map</u> – teacher – tie
  3. coat – carrot – <u>bed</u> – cookie
  4. <u>rug</u> – dime – dollar – desk
  5. sofa – soup – soda – <u>pen</u>

PHONEMIC AWARENESS 2:
Initial Consonant Sounds (with Pictures)

1. **PHONEME ISOLATION** Have students look at the first picture in the top (sample exercise) row. Ask: "What is this?" (A pen.) Ask: "What's the first sound in *pen*?" (/p/) (Say it as a sound, not the name of the letter "P".) Do the same for the third and fourth words, *pencil* and *penny*.

2. **PHONEME IDENTIFICATION** Ask: "What sound is the same in *pen*, *pencil*, and *penny*?" (/p/; the first sound)

3. **PHONEME CATEGORIZATION** Do the following three times as students listen carefully. Say all four words in the top row and ask: "Listen. Which word does not belong? *pen, ruler, pencil, penny*." (*ruler*) Ask students why the word doesn't belong. (It starts with a different sound.)

4. **MARKING THE ANSWER** Demonstrate how to mark an X on the picture of the ruler in order to show that this word is different from the others. Have students trace over the X on the ruler, and circulate around the classroom to check their work.

5. **EXERCISES 1–5** For the first one or two exercises on the worksheet, do all four steps above in order to assure students are grasping the phonemic awareness concept and developing the required skills. For the rest of the exercises, go immediately to step 3 and have students mark their answers.

6. **PHONEME BLENDING** For additional practice with these pictures, have students listen as you say in sequence the separate sounds that make up one of these words, and have students listen and then say the word. For example: "What word is this? /p/, /e/, /n/" (*pen*) (Reminder: Say the sounds, not the names of the letters.) For an easy version of this activity, tell students the row where the picture of the word is located. For a more challenging version, have students scan the entire worksheet.

Script and Answer Key:
 Ex: pen – <u>ruler</u> – pencil – penny
  1. bed – banana – book – <u>rug</u>
  2. lamp – lettuce – <u>notebook</u> – lemonade
  3. peach – <u>carrot</u> – pizza – potato
  4. <u>tomato</u> – soup – soda – sandwich
  5. taco – tie – table – <u>milk</u>

PHONEMIC AWARENESS 3:
Initial Consonant Sounds (with Names)

This worksheet combines phonemic awareness with early decoding skills, using first names as the context for letter-sound recognition. It can be used in conjunction with *Foundations* Unit 1 or prior to that in conjunction with the worksheets in Preliteracy Practice 19 focusing on writing lowercase manuscript letters. Prior to or after using Phonemic Awareness Worksheet 3, it may be helpful to have students do a similar worksheet you create using the first names of students in the class.

1. **PHONEME ISOLATION** Have students look at the first name in the top (sample exercise) row. Ask: "What is this name?" (*Bob*) Ask: "What's the first sound in *Bob*?" (/b/) (Say it as a sound, not the name of the letter "B".) Do the same for the second and third names, *Bill* and *Ben*.

2. **PHONEME IDENTIFICATION** Ask: "What sound is the same in *Bob*, *Bill*, and *Ben*?" (/b/; the first sound)

3. **PHONEME CATEGORIZATION** Do the following three times as students listen carefully. Say all four names in the top row and ask: "Listen. Which name does not belong? *Bob, Bill, Ben, Ron*" (*Ron*) Ask students why the name doesn't belong. (It starts with a different sound.)

4. **MARKING THE ANSWER** Demonstrate how to mark an X on the name "Ron" in order to show that this name is different from the others. Have students trace over the X on the name, and circulate around the classroom to check their work.

5. **EXERCISES 1–5** For the first one or two exercises on the worksheet, do all four steps above in order to assure students are grasping the phonemic awareness concept and developing the required skills. For the rest of the exercises, go immediately to step 3 and have students mark their answers.

6. **PHONEME BLENDING** For additional practice with these names, have students listen as you say in sequence the separate sounds that make up one of these names, and have students listen and then say the name. For example: "What name is this? /b/, /e/, /n/" (*Ben*) (Reminder: Say the sounds, not the names of the letters.) For an easy version of this activity, tell students the row where the name is located. For a more challenging version, have students scan the entire worksheet.

Script and Answer Key:
Ex: Bob – Bill – Ben – <u>Ron</u>
 1. Jan – <u>Len</u> – Jon – Jen
 2. Mike – Maria – <u>Sam</u> – Mel
 3. <u>Gil</u> – Don – Dan – Dave
 4. Ken – <u>Pat</u> – Kate – Karl
 5. Nick – Nancy – Neil – <u>Tim</u>
 6. Sue – Sam – <u>Henry</u> – Sally

PHONEMIC AWARENESS 4:
Phoneme Segmentation (with Unit 2 Vocabulary)

This worksheet can be used in conjunction with *Foundations* Unit 2 since it incorporates vocabulary in that unit, or it can be used prior to that in conjunction with the worksheets in Preliteracy Practice 20 focusing on writing numbers.

1. **SAMPLE EXERCISE 1** Say in sequence the separate sounds that make up the word in the first exercise, and then blend the sounds together as you say the word slowly. (/b/, /u/, /k/ *book*) Do this three times. Ask students: "How many sounds do you hear in this word?" (Three.) "What are the sounds?" (/b/, /u/, /k/) "What is the word?" (*book*)

2. **WRITING THE ANSWER** Demonstrate how to write the answer by writing a numeral "3" on the line below the picture. (The sample answer is provided for Exercise 1.)

3. **PHONEME SEGMENTATION (EXERCISES 2–3)** For the next two exercises on the worksheet, say in sequence the separate sounds that make up the word, and then blend the sounds together as you say the word slowly. Do this three times. Ask students: "How many sounds do you hear in this word?" "What are the sounds?" "What is the word?" Have students write the answer on the line below the picture.
Exercise 2: /m/, /a/, /p/ – map – 3 sounds
Exercise 3: /k/, /l/, /o/, /k/ – clock – 4 sounds

4. **PHONEME SEGMENTATION (EXERCISES 4–9)** Don't say the separate sounds in these words. Say the complete word slowly three times. Have students write the number of sounds they hear in the word. After each exercise, ask students: "How many sounds do you hear in this word?" "What are the sounds?" "What is the word?"

5. **PHONEME BLENDING** For additional practice with these words, have students listen as you say in sequence the separate sounds that make up one of the nine words on the page, and have students listen and then say the word. For example: "What word is this? /d/, /e/, /s/, /k/" (*desk*) (Reminder: Say the sounds, not the names of the letters.)

Answer Key (Word, number of sounds):
1. book (3)
2. map (3)
3. clock (4)
4. pen (3)
5. globe (4)
6. chair (3) (Note: /ch/ is a single sound)
7. desk (4)
8. sit (3)
9. screen (5)

PHONEMIC AWARENESS 5:
Phoneme Segmentation (with Unit 3 Vocabulary)

This worksheet can be used in conjunction with *Foundations* Unit 3 since it incorporates vocabulary in that unit, or it can be used prior to that in conjunction with the worksheets in Preliteracy Practice 20 focusing on writing numbers.

1. **SAMPLE EXERCISE 1** Say in sequence the separate sounds that make up the word in the first exercise, and then blend the sounds together as you say the word slowly. (/ee/, /t/ *eat*) Do this three times. Ask students: "How many sounds do you hear in this word?" (Two.) "What are the sounds?" (/ee/, /t/) "What is the word?" (*eat*)

2. **WRITING THE ANSWER** Demonstrate how to write the answer by writing a numeral "2" on the line below the picture. (The sample answer is provided for Exercise 1.)

3. **PHONEME SEGMENTATION (EXERCISES 2–3)** For the next two exercises on the worksheet, say in sequence the separate sounds that make up the word, and then blend the sounds together as you say the word slowly. Do this three times. Ask students: "How many sounds do you hear in this word?" "What are the sounds?" "What is the word?" Have students write the answer on the line below the picture.
   Exercise 2: /k/, /u/, /k/ – cook – 3 sounds
   Exercise 3: /r/, /ee/, /d/ – read – 3 sounds

4. **PHONEME SEGMENTATION (EXERCISES 4–9)** Don't say the separate sounds in these words. Say the complete word slowly three times. Have students write the number of sounds they hear in the word. After each exercise, ask students: "How many sounds do you hear in this word?" "What are the sounds?" "What is the word?"

5. **PHONEME BLENDING** For additional practice with these words, have students listen as you say in sequence the separate sounds that make up one of the nine words on the page, and have students listen and then say the word. For example: "What word is this? /h/, /o/, /t/" (*hot*) (Reminder: Say the sounds, not the names of the letters.)

Answer Key (Word, number of sounds):
1. eat (2)
2. cook (3)
3. read (3)
4. clean (4)
5. wash (3) (Note: /sh/ is a single sound)
6. play (3)
7. hot (3)
8. rain (3)
9. cold (4)

PHONEMIC AWARENESS 1
Initial Consonant Sounds
(with Pictures)

Student's Name _____

Date _____

LISTEN. PUT AN X.

1.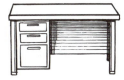

2.

3.

4.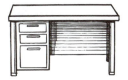

5.

(Instructions: For each exercise, read aloud the series of words slowly three times and have students put an X on the picture of the word that is different because it starts with a different initial consonant. See the Answer Key for the script, answers, and additional phonemic awareness activities for this worksheet.)

Foundations
Phonemic Awareness Worksheet 1

PHONEMIC AWARENESS 2
Initial Consonant Sounds
(with Pictures)

Student's Name _____

Date _____

LISTEN. PUT AN X.

 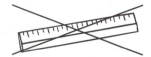 

1.

2.

3.

4.

5.

(Instructions: For each exercise, read aloud the series of words slowly three times and have students put an X on the picture of the word that is different because it starts with a different initial consonant. See the Answer Key for the script, answers, and additional phonemic awareness activities for this worksheet.)

PHONEMIC AWARENESS 3
Initial Consonant Sounds
(with Names)

Student's Name _____

Date _____

LISTEN. PUT AN X.

| | Bob | Bill | Ben | ~~Ron~~ |

1. | Jan | Len | Jon | Jen |

2. | Mike | Maria | Sam | Mel |

3. | Gil | Don | Dan | Dave |

4. | Ken | Pat | Kate | Karl |

5. | Nick | Nancy | Neil | Tim |

6. | Sue | Sam | Henry | Sally |

(Instructions: For each exercise, read aloud the series of names slowly three times and have students put an X on the name that is different because it starts with a different initial consonant. See the Answer Key for the answers and additional phonemic awareness activities for this worksheet.)

PHONEMIC AWARENESS 4
Phoneme Segmentation
(with Unit 2 Vocabulary)

Student's Name _____

Date _____

LISTEN. COUNT THE SOUNDS.

1. __3__

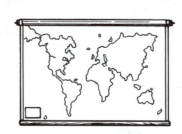

2. _____

3. _____

4. _____

5. _____

6. _____

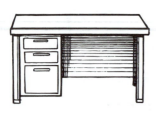

7. _____

8. _____

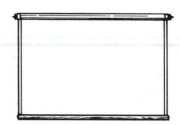

9. _____

(Instructions: For each exercise, say the word slowly three times and have students write the number of sounds they hear in the word. For the first exercise, demonstrate the concept by first saying each sound of the word separately and then blending the sounds together as you say the word slowly. You can continue this way with some additional exercises for students who need more guided practice with phoneme segmentation. See the Answer Key for the script, answers, and additional phonemic awareness activities for this worksheet.)

PHONEMIC AWARENESS 5
Phoneme Segmentation
(with Unit 3 Vocabulary)

Student's Name _____

Date _____

LISTEN. COUNT THE SOUNDS.

1. _2_

2. _____

3. _____

4. _____

5. _____

6. _____

7. _____

8. _____

9. _____

(Instructions: For each exercise, say the word slowly three times and have students write the number of sounds they hear in the word. For the first exercise, demonstrate the concept by first saying each sound of the word separately and then blending the sounds together as you say the word slowly. You can continue this way with some additional exercises for students who need more guided practice with phoneme segmentation. See the Answer Key for the script, answers, and additional phonemic awareness activities for this worksheet.)

Foundations
Phonemic Awareness Worksheet 5

FOUNDATIONS
PRELITERACY PRACTICE

The *Foundations* Preliteracy Practice Worksheets are designed for students who do not have basic literacy skills in any language. The worksheets provide a careful sequence of instruction that develops students' basic preliteracy concepts and skills as described in the Table of Contents below. Through this practice, students also develop the basic concepts of a left-to-right and top-to-bottom progression for decoding English text. They also develop the ability to hold a writing utensil—first to draw lines and shapes, then to learn the basic strokes that make up letters, and finally to develop handwriting skills to trace and copy upper case and lower case letters and numbers.

Since these may be among the first worksheets your students use in your instructional program, you can use these activities to introduce the basic concept of the top-to-bottom and left-to-right orientation of English text on a page. It may be helpful to have students use a separate blank sheet of paper to mask all page content below the exercise line they are working with. After students complete that line, they can move their blank paper down to reveal the next exercise.

In addition to these Preliteracy Practice Worksheets and other resources on this CD-ROM, the *Foundations* Literacy Workbook offers extensive practice designed for low-beginning students who have limited or no literacy skills.

PRELITERACY PRACTICE CONTENTS

PRELITERACY PRACTICE 1

TRACE.

 -

 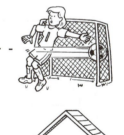

Concepts about Print: Left to Right, Top to Bottom

PRELITERACY PRACTICE 2

Student's Name _____

Date _____

PUT AN **X** ON THE DIFFERENT SHAPE.

1.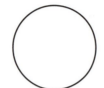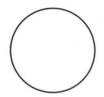

2.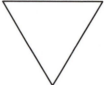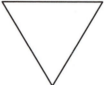

3.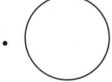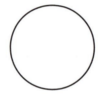

4.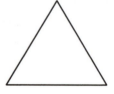

5.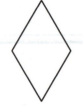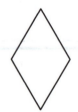

6.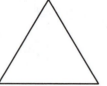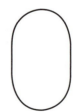

PRELITERACY PRACTICE 3

Student's Name _____

Date _____

PUT AN **X** ON THE DIFFERENT SHAPE.

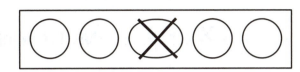

1.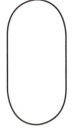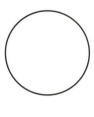

2.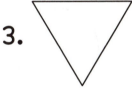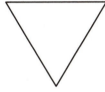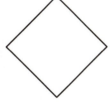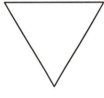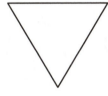

3.

4.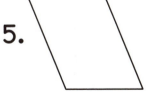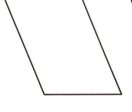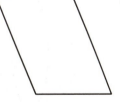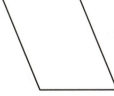

5.

6.

PRELITERACY PRACTICE 4   Student's Name _____

Date _____

PUT AN **X** ON THE ONE THAT IS DIFFERENT.

1.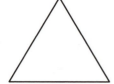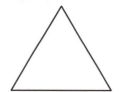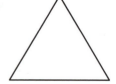

2.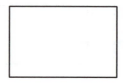

3.

4.

5.

6.

Identifying Different Sizes of Shapes

PRELITERACY PRACTICE 5   Student's Name _____

Date _____

PUT AN **X** ON THE ONE THAT IS DIFFERENT.

1.

2.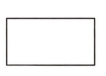

3.

4.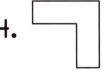

5.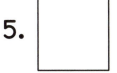

6.

Identifying Different Shapes by Directionality

PRELITERACY PRACTICE 6

Student's Name _____

Date _____

CIRCLE THE SAME SHAPE.

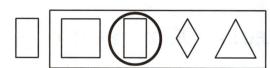

1.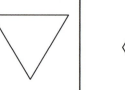

2.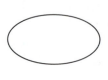

3.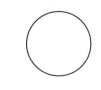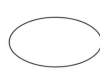

4.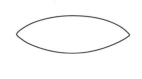

5.

6.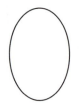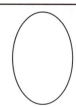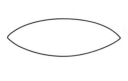

Identifying Same Shapes (Easy)

PRELITERACY PRACTICE 7

Student's Name _____

Date _____

CIRCLE THE SAME SHAPE.

1.

2.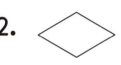

3.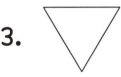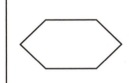

4.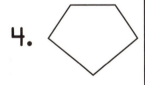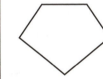

5.

6.

Identifying Same Shapes (More Difficult)

PRELITERACY PRACTICE 8

Student's Name _____

Date _____

CIRCLE THE ONE THAT IS THE SAME.

1.

2.

3.

4.

5.

6.

Identifying Same Sizes of Shapes

PRELITERACY PRACTICE 9

Student's Name _____

Date _____

CIRCLE THE ONE THAT IS THE SAME.

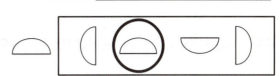

1.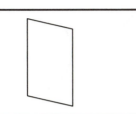

2.

3.

4. V

5. L

6. J

Identifying Same Shapes by Directionality

PRELITERACY PRACTICE 10   Student's Name _____

Date _____

PUT AN **X** ON THE ONE THAT IS DIFFERENT.

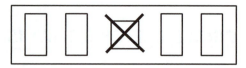

1.

2.

3.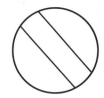

4.

5.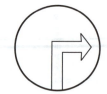

6. 55 55 22 55 55

Foundations
Preliteracy Practice 10

Identifying Different Signs

© 2007 Pearson Education, Inc.
Duplication for classroom use is permitted.

PRELITERACY PRACTICE 11   Student's Name _____

Date _____

PUT AN X ON THE DIFFERENT LETTER.

1. T T T S T T T

2. C C C V C C C

3. I I G I I I I

4. A J A A A A A

5. O O N O O O O

6. Z U Z Z Z Z Z

Identifying Different Block Letters (Easy)

PRELITERACY PRACTICE 12   Student's Name _____

Date _____

PUT AN X ON THE DIFFERENT LETTER.

C C ⊗ C C C

1. V V A V V V

2. F F F F E F

3. W W M W W W

4. O O O Q O O

5. T I T T T T

6. P P P R P P

Identifying Different Block Letters (More Difficult)

Student's Name _____

Date _____

CIRCLE THE SAME LETTERS.

P P B P R D P

1. F H V F A G F

2. J J L K C J J

3. S U M C S T S

4. B B Z B O A B

5. Y M Y L Y P E

6. R R N R B P R

Identifying Same Block Letters (Easy)

PRELITERACY PRACTICE 14   Student's Name _____

Date _____

CIRCLE THE SAME LETTERS.

1. C   O   C   G   C   Q   O

2. R   B   P   R   K   R   R

3. d   b   p   h   d   b   d

4. e   c   e   o   e   a   c

5. M   M   W   M   N   W   M

6. q   d   g   q   p   b   q

Identifying Different Smaller Letters

PRELITERACY PRACTICE 15   Student's Name _____

Date _____

PUT AN **X** ON THE DIFFERENT LETTER.   S S ⊗ S S

1. L L L L A L L

2. E J E E E E E

3. Y Y Y Y V Y Y

4. W W W W W M W

5. P P P P P P R

6. T T I T T T T

7. O O O Q O O O

8. p p p q p p p

9. b d d d d d d

10. h h n h h h h

Identifying Different Smaller Letters

PRELITERACY PRACTICE 16   Student's Name _____

Date _____

CIRCLE THE SAME LETTERS.

A A V K A N Y

1. H   H I T H E I

2. A   V A Y X A V

3. G   C O G C G O

4. R   P R B R R P

5. T   E I T F T I

6. X   X K X Y W X

7. N   M V N W N M

8. p   q p b p d q

9. j   i y j i j j

10. h   n k h m h b

Identifying Same Smaller Letters

STARTING STROKES

TRACE.

I I I I I B B B B

D D D D E E E E

F F F F H H H H

I I I I K K K L L L L

P P P R R R T T T

M M M M N N N N

Writing Readiness: Basic Strokes

TRACE.

/ / / / / / / A A A A

M M M V V V V W W W

X X X X Z Z Z Z

/ / / / / / / A A A A

M M M M N N N N V V

W W W W X X X X

Writing Readiness: Basic Strokes

TRACE.

A A A

E E E F F F H H H

L L L T T T Z Z Z

C C C G G G

O O O Q Q Q

D D D D

Writing Readiness: Basic Strokes

Student's Name _____

Date _____

TRACE.

P P P P P P P P P P P

R R R R R B B B B B

/ / / / / K K K Y Y Y

J J J J J J J J J J J

U U U U U U U U U U U

S S S S S S S S S S

Writing Readiness: Basic Strokes

Student's Name _____

Date _____

UPPER CASE LETTERS

TRACE.

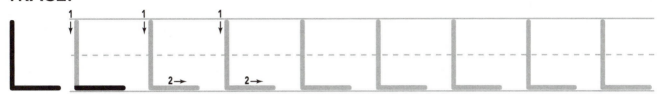

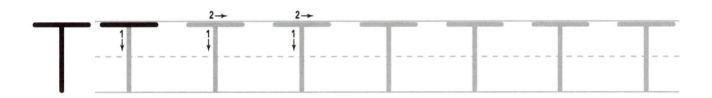

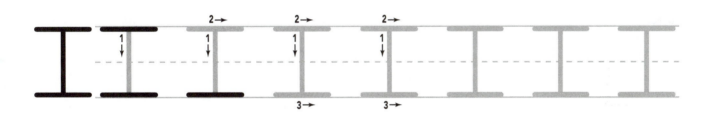

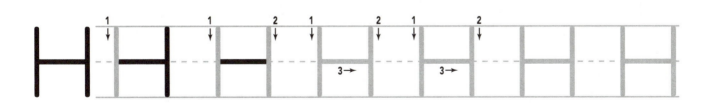

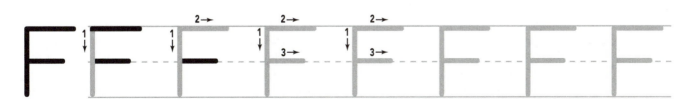

Upper Case Letters: Manuscript

TRACE AND COPY.

L L L L L L L L L L L L L

L

T T T T T T T T T T T T

T

I I I I I I I I I I I I

I

H H H H H H H H H H H

H

F F F F F F F F F F F

F

Upper Case Letters: Manuscript

TRACE.

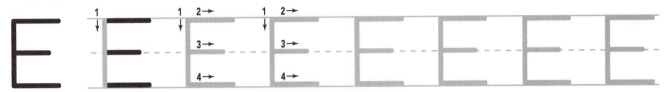

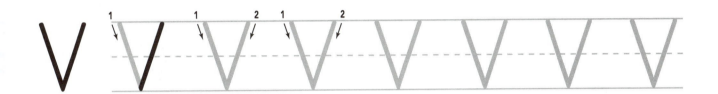

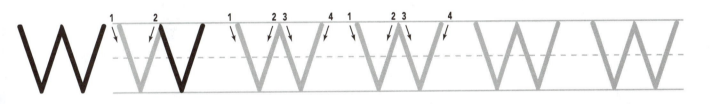

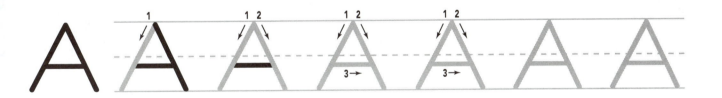

Upper Case Letters: Manuscript

TRACE AND COPY.

E E E E E E E E E E E

E

V V V V V V V V V

V

W W W W W W W W W

W

A A A A A A A A A A

A

X X X X X X X X X

X

Upper Case Letters: Manuscript

TRACE.

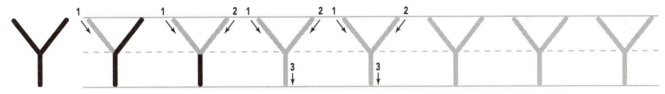

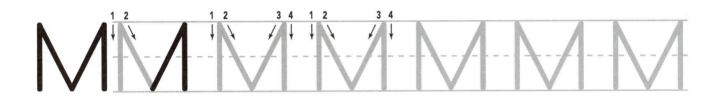

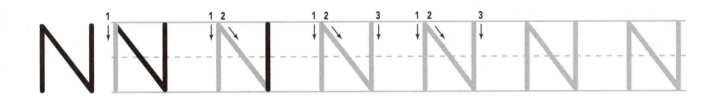

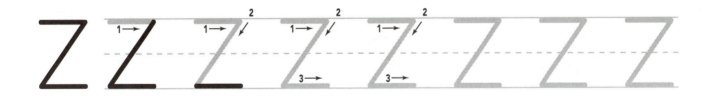

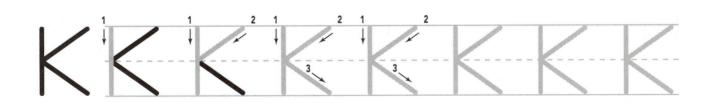

Upper Case Letters: Manuscript

Student's Name _____

Date _____

TRACE AND COPY.

Y Y Y Y Y Y Y Y Y Y Y

Y

M M M M M M M M M M M

M

N N N N N N N N N N N

N

Z Z Z Z Z Z Z Z Z Z Z

Z

K K K K K K K K K K K

K

Upper Case Letters: Manuscript

Student's Name _____

Date _____

TRACE.

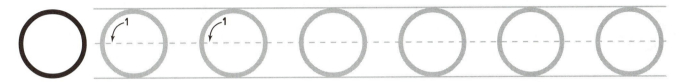

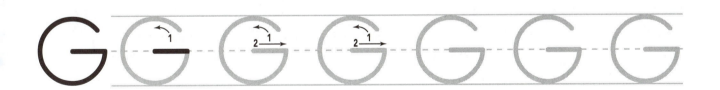

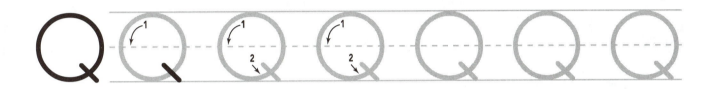

S S S S S S S S

Upper Case Letters: Manuscript

TRACE AND COPY.

O O O O O O O O O O

O

Q Q Q Q Q Q Q Q Q Q

Q

C C C C C C C C C C

C

G G G G G G G G G G

G

S S S S S S S S S S

S

Upper Case Letters: Manuscript

Student's Name _____

Date _____

TRACE.

U U U U U U U U U U U U

J J J J J J J J J J J J

D D D D D D D D D D D D

P P P P P P P P P P P P

B B B B B B B B B B B B

R R R R R R R R R R R R

Upper Case Letters: Manuscript

TRACE AND COPY.

U U U U U U U U U U U

U

J J J J J J J J J J J

J

D D D D D D D D D D

D

P P P P P P P P P P

P

B B B B B B B B B B

B

R R R R R R R R R R R

R

Upper Case Letters: Manuscript

Student's Name _____

Date _____

TRACE AND COPY.

L L _____ Z Z _____

T T _____ K K _____

I I _____ O O _____

H H _____ Q Q _____

F F _____ C C _____

E E _____ G G _____

V V _____ S S _____

W W _____ U U _____

A A _____ J J _____

X X _____ D D _____

Y Y _____ P P _____

M M _____ B B _____

N N _____ R R _____

Upper Case Letters: Manuscript

PRELITERACY PRACTICE 19a

Student's Name _____

Date _____

LOWER CASE LETTERS

TRACE.

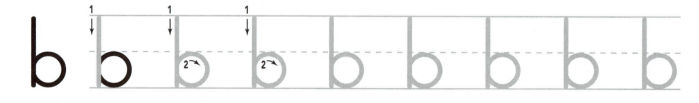

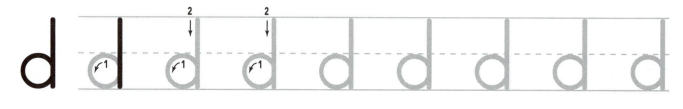

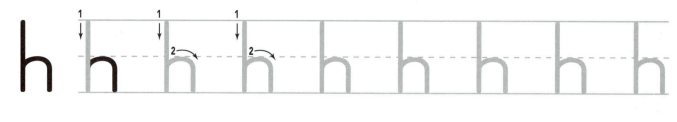

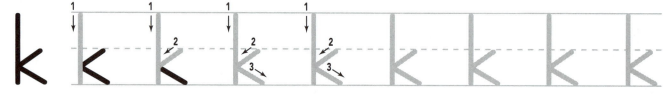

Lower Case Letters: Manuscript

Student's Name _____

Date _____

TRACE AND COPY.

l
l l l l l l l l

l

b
b b b b b b b b b

b

d
d d d d d d d d d

d

h
h h h h h h h h h

h

k
k k k k k k k k k

k

f
f f f f f f f f f

f

t
t t t t t t t t t

t

Lower Case Letters: Manuscript

PRELITERACY PRACTICE 19c

Student's Name _____

Date _____

TRACE.

o   o   o   o   o   o   o   o   o

c   c   c   c   c   c   c   c   c

e   e   e   e   e   e   e   e   e

a   a   a   a   a   a   a   a   a

n   n   n   n   n   n   n   n   n

m   m   m   m   m   m   m   m   m

u   u   u   u   u   u   u   u   u

Foundations
Preliteracy Practice 19c (#3 of 11)

Lower Case Letters: Manuscript

TRACE AND COPY.

o   o   o   o   o   o   o   o   o   o

o

c   c   c   c   c   c   c   c   c   c

c

e   e   e   e   e   e   e   e   e   e

e

a   a   a   a   a   a   a   a   a   a

a

n   n   n   n   n   n   n   n   n   n

n

m   m   m   m   m   m   m   m   m   m

m

u   u   u   u   u   u   u   u   u   u

u

Lower Case Letters: Manuscript

Student's Name _____

Date _____

TRACE.

V V V V V V V V V V

W W W W W W W W W W

x x x x x x x x x x

z z z z z z z z z z

i i i i i i i i i i

r r r r r r r r r r

s s s s s s s s s s

Lower Case Letters: Manuscript

TRACE AND COPY.

v   v   v   v   v   v   v   v   v   v

v

w   w   w   w   w   w   w   w   w

w

x   x   x   x   x   x   x   x   x   x

x

z   z   z   z   z   z   z   z   z   z

z

i   i   i   i   i   i   i   i   i   i

i

r   r   r   r   r   r   r   r   r   r

r

s   s   s   s   s   s   s   s   s   s

s

Lower Case Letters: Manuscript

Student's Name _____

Date _____

TRACE.

p p p p p p p p p

q q q q q q q q q

g g g g g g g g g

j j j j j j j j j

y y y y y y y y y

Lower Case Letters: Manuscript

Student's Name _____

Date _____

TRACE AND COPY.

p p p p p p p p p p p

p

q q q q q q q q q q q

q

g g g g g g g g g g g

g

j j j j j j j j j j j

j

y y y y y y y y y y y

y

Lower Case Letters: Manuscript

TRACE AND COPY THE ALPHABET.

a a _____   n n _____

b b _____   o o _____

c c _____   p p _____

d d _____   q q _____

e e _____   r r _____

f f _____   s s _____

g g _____   t t _____

h h _____   u u _____

i i _____   v v _____

j j _____   w w _____

k k _____   x x _____

l l _____   y y _____

m m _____   z z _____

Lower Case Letters: Manuscript

TRACE AND COPY THE ALPHABET.

Aa Aa Aa

Bb Bb Bb

Cc Cc Cc

Dd Dd Dd

Ee Ee Ee

Ff Ff Ff

Gg Gg Gg

Hh Hh Hh

Ii Ii Ii

Jj Jj Jj

Kk Kk Kk

Ll Ll Ll

Mm Mm Mm

Lower Case Letters: Manuscript

TRACE AND COPY THE ALPHABET.

Nn   Nn Nn

Oo   Oo Oo

Pp   Pp Pp

Qq   Qq Qq

Rr   Rr Rr

Ss   Ss Ss

Tt   Tt Tt

Uu   Uu Uu

Vv   Vv Vv

Ww   Ww Ww

Xx   Xx Xx

Yy   Yy Yy

Zz   Zz Zz

Lower Case Letters: Manuscript

NUMBERS

TRACE.

1 1 1 1 1 1 1 1 1 1

2 2 2 2 2 2 2 2 2 2

3 3 3 3 3 3 3 3 3 3

4 4 4 4 4 4 4 4 4 4

5 5 5 5 5 5 5 5 5 5

TRACE AND COPY.

1

1

2 2 2 2 2 2 2 2 2 2 2

2

3 3 3 3 3 3 3 3 3 3 3

3

4 4 4 4 4 4 4 4 4 4 4

4

5 5 5 5 5 5 5 5 5 5 5

5

Numbers

TRACE.

6 6 6 6 6 6 6 6 6

7 7 7 7 7 7 7 7 7

8 8 8 8 8 8 8 8 8

9 9 9 9 9 9 9 9 9

10 10 10 10 10 10

Numbers

TRACE AND COPY.

6 6 6 6 6 6 6 6 6 6 6

6

7 7 7 7 7 7 7 7 7 7 7

7

8 8 8 8 8 8 8 8 8 8 8

8

9 9 9 9 9 9 9 9 9 9 9

9

10 10 10 10 10 10 10 10 10 10 10

10

Numbers

FOUNDATIONS
LITERACY PRACTICE INSTRUCTIONS & ANSWER KEY

Note to Teachers:

The *Foundations* Literacy Practice Worksheets are mostly picture-word recognition activities in simple matching and multiple-choice formats. The worksheets provide students with basic literacy practice and preparation for the types of questions found on standards-based tests at the beginning literacy level. Two multiple-choice formats of varying difficulty are included in each unit. In the easier format, students see a word and four pictures and they select the correct picture to match the word. In the more challenging format, students see a picture and they select the correct one of four words or expressions to match the picture. Units 1 and 11 Worksheets also include practice with recognition of uppercase and lowercase letters in both manuscript and cursive forms.

UNIT 1

Literacy Practice A
1. g
2. w
3. b
4. f
5. m
6. h
7. p
8. a

Literacy Practice B
1. V
2. I
3. M
4. b
5. h

Literacy Practice C
1. g
2. d
3. n
4. a
5. U

Literacy Practice D
1. last
2. nine
3. ten
4. six
5. name

Literacy Practice E
1. Anna Ramos
2. 4 Main St.
3. Los Angeles
4. California
5. 90036
6. 2F
7. (323) 456-8917
8. 226-37-4189

Literacy Practice F
1. C
2. A
3. B
4. A
5. D

UNIT 2

Literacy Practice A
1. book
2. pencil
3. map
4. ruler
5. eraser
6. computer
7. pen
8. globe

Literacy Practice B
1. B
2. D
3. C
4. A

Literacy Practice C
1. D
2. C
3. A
4. B
5. C
6. B

UNIT 3

Literacy Practice A
1. I get up.
2. I brush my teeth.
3. I eat breakfast.
4. I take a shower.
5. I read.
6. I exercise.
7. I clean.
8. I watch TV.

Literacy Practice B
1. It's cloudy.
2. It's hot.
3. It's cold.
4. It's sunny.
5. It's snowing.
6. It's raining.
7. It's foggy.

Literacy Practice C
1. D
2. A
3. C
4. D

Literacy Practice D
1. B
2. A
3. A
4. C
5. D
6. B

UNIT 4

Literacy Practice A
1. Saturday
2. Monday
3. Thursday
4. Sunday
5. Wednesday
6. Friday
7. Tuesday

Literacy Practice B
1. March
2. December
3. May
4. July
5. October
6. August
7. April
8. November
9. January
10. June
11. September
12. February

Literacy Practice C
1. C
2. D
3. B
4. C
5. A
6. D

Literacy Practice D
1. C
2. A
3. D
4. B
5. D
6. C

UNIT 5

Literacy Practice A
1. lamp
2. table
3. sofa
4. bed
5. rug
6. chair
7. refrigerator

Literacy Practice B
1. B
2. A
3. D
4. C

Literacy Practice C
1. D
2. A
3. C
4. B
5. A
6. D

UNIT 6

Literacy Practice A
1. bank
2. gas station
3. library
4. post office
5. supermarket
6. laundromat
7. department store
8. hospital

Literacy Practice B
1. B
2. A
3. D
4. C

Literacy Practice C
1. B
2. D
3. A
4. D
5. C
6. A

UNIT 7

Literacy Practice A
1. hungry
2. thirsty
3. sick
4. tired
5. afraid
6. happy
7. angry
8. sad

Literacy Practice B
1. A
2. C
3. B
4. D

Literacy Practice C
1. C
2. B
3. D
4. B
5. A
6. D

UNIT 8

Literacy Practice A
1. banana
2. cookie
3. carrot
4. apple
5. potato
6. tomato
7. egg
8. onion

Literacy Practice B
1. D
2. C
3. A
4. B

Literacy Practice C
1. C
2. B
3. D
4. A
5. B
6. C

UNIT 9

Literacy Practice A
1. blouse
2. umbrella
3. tie
4. dress
5. jacket
6. watch
7. suit
8. necklace

Literacy Practice B
1. B
2. A
3. D
4. C

Literacy Practice C
1. A
2. C
3. D
4. B
5. C
6. A

UNIT 10

Literacy Practice A
1. stamps
2. check
3. checkbook
4. package
5. credit card
6. money order
7. bank book
8. air letter

Literacy Practice B
1. C
2. D
3. A
4. B

Literacy Practice C
1. B
2. C
3. A
4. B
5. D
6. C

UNIT 11

Literacy Practice A
1. stomachache
2. headache
3. cough
4. toothache
5. cold
6. fever
7. backache

Literacy Practice B
1. D
2. B
3. A
4. B

Literacy Practice C
1. D
2. B
3. C
4. B
5. A
6. D

Literacy Practice D
1. L
2. G
3. I
4. Z
5. f
6. k
7. t
8. n

Literacy Practice E
1. *a*
2. *s*
3. *j*
4. *jb*
5. *d*
6. *r*
7. *q*
8. *f*

Literacy Practice F
1. M
2. T
3. E
4. f
5. h
6. z

Literacy Practice G
1. *e*
2. *g*
3. *h*
4. *L*
5. *m*
6. *2*

UNIT 12

Literacy Practice A
1. science
2. math
3. English
4. music
5. art
6. technology
7. social studies

Literacy Practice B
1. B
2. A
3. D
4. C

Literacy Practice C
1. D
2. A
3. C
4. B
5. D
6. B

UNIT 13

Literacy Practice A
1. cashier
2. electrician
3. cook
4. security guard
5. construction worker
6. repairperson
7. gardener
8. delivery person

Literacy Practice B
1. B
2. C
3. A
4. D

Literacy Practice C
1. B
2. D
3. C
4. A
5. D
6. B

UNIT 14

Literacy Practice A
1. Stop
2. No left turn
3. No right turn
4. School nearby
5. Train tracks ahead
6. No U-turn
7. People in the street

Literacy Practice B
1. C
2. A
3. D
4. B

Literacy Practice C
1. C
2. B
3. A
4. C
5. D
6. B

UNIT 15

Literacy Practice A
1. see a movie
2. go swimming
3. go to a museum
4. go jogging
5. go dancing
6. exercise
7. go to a concert

Literacy Practice B
1. B
2. C
3. A
4. D

Literacy Practice C
1. D
2. A
3. C
4. B
5. B
6. D

Student's Name _____

Date _____

MATCH.

1. G   b

2. W   m

3. B   w

4. F   p

5. M   h

6. H   g

7. P   a

8. A   f

Student's Name _____

Date _____

CIRCLE THE CORRECT LETTER.

R

    B   P   (R)   E

1. V

    Y   U   W   V

2. I

    J   I   L   T

3. M

    M   W   N   V

4. b

    p   d   b   q

5. h

    n   m   b   h

Student's Name _____

Date _____

CIRCLE THE CORRECT LETTER.

K

h   (k)   f   d

1. G

c   j   g   a

2. D

d   b   h   q

3. N

m   h   u   n

4. A

v   a   u   x

5. u

W   V   U   N

Student's Name _____

Date _____

CIRCLE THE CORRECT WORD.

name

game   fame   (name)   mane

1. last

   list   lost   lest   last

2. nine

   nine   line   mine   dine

3. ten

   hen   den   ten   pen

4. six

   mix   fix   nix   six

5. NAME

   nice   meet   mane   name

Student's Name _____

Date _____

MATCH.

1. name   90036

2. address   California

3. city   2F

4. state   4 Main St.

5. zip code   226-37-4189

6. apartment number   Los Angeles

7. telephone number   Anna Ramos

8. social security number   (323) 456-8917

Student's Name _____

Date _____

CHOOSE THE ANSWER.

8 Main Street

- (A) city
- **(B) address**
- (C) name
- (D) zip code

90036

1.
- (A) state
- (B) city
- (C) zip code
- (D) telephone number

Linda Chen

2.
- (A) name
- (B) city
- (C) state
- (D) address

(646) 782-3394

3.
- (A) apartment number
- (B) telephone number
- (C) social security number
- (D) zip code

Los Angeles

4.
- (A) city
- (B) name
- (C) address
- (D) state

027-38-5196

5.
- (A) zip code
- (B) apartment number
- (C) telephone number
- (D) social security number

Student's Name _____

Date _____

MATCH.

1.

2.

3.

4.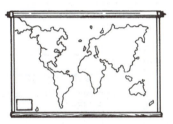

5.

6.

7.

8.

map

eraser

pencil

computer

book

globe

ruler

pen

Student's Name _____

Date _____

ruler

1.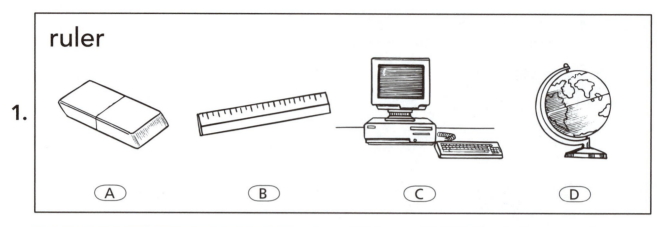

A   B   C   D

desk

2.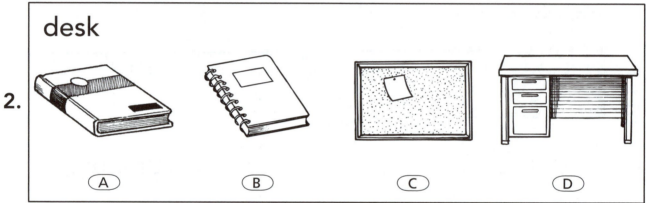

A   B   C   D

board

3.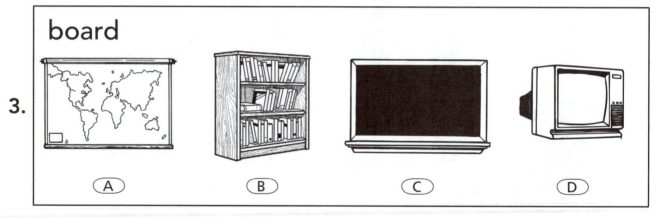

A   B   C   D

chalk

4.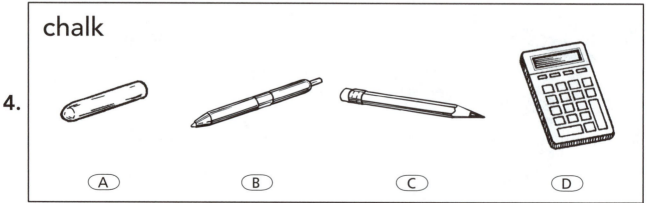

A   B   C   D

Student's Name _____

Date _____

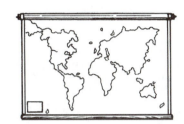

1. Ⓐ ruler
   Ⓑ board
   Ⓒ globe
   Ⓓ map

2. Ⓐ pen
   Ⓑ chalk
   Ⓒ pencil
   Ⓓ eraser

3. Ⓐ computer
   Ⓑ ruler
   Ⓒ projector
   Ⓓ calculator

4. Ⓐ bookshelf
   Ⓑ notebook
   Ⓒ board
   Ⓓ desk

5. Ⓐ projector
   Ⓑ computer
   Ⓒ TV
   Ⓓ calculator

6. Ⓐ notebook
   Ⓑ bookshelf
   Ⓒ desk
   Ⓓ bulletin board

Student's Name _____

Date _____

MATCH.

1. I eat breakfast.

2. I exercise.

3. I brush my teeth.

4. I watch TV.

5. I clean.

6. I read.

7. I get up.

8. I take a shower.

Student's Name _____

Date _____

MATCH.

1.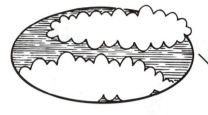

        It's cold.

2.

        It's snowing.

3.

        It's cloudy.

4.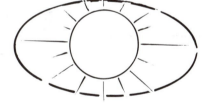

        It's raining.

5.

        It's sunny.

6.

        It's foggy.

7.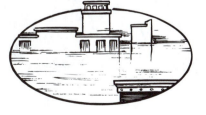

        It's hot.

Student's Name _____

Date _____

read

1.   A   B   C   D

wash the dishes

2.   A   B   C   D

cook dinner

3.   A   B   C   D

comb my hair

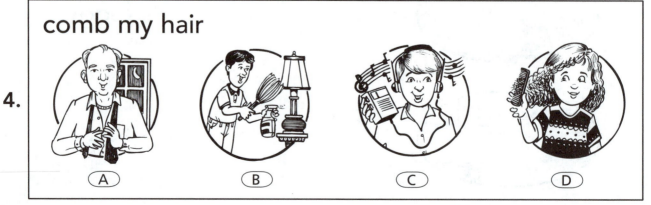

4.   A   B   C   D

Student's Name _____

Date _____

1. Ⓐ take a shower

Ⓑ brush my teeth

Ⓒ comb my hair

Ⓓ wash the dishes

2. Ⓐ go to bed

Ⓑ get up

Ⓒ exercise

Ⓓ get dressed

3. Ⓐ do the laundry

Ⓑ come home

Ⓒ study

Ⓓ go to school

4. Ⓐ eat breakfast

Ⓑ read

Ⓒ make lunch

Ⓓ eat dinner

5. Ⓐ listen to music

Ⓑ watch TV

Ⓒ play basketball

Ⓓ play the guitar

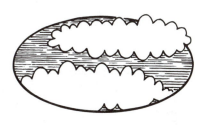

6. Ⓐ snowing

Ⓑ cloudy

Ⓒ sunny

Ⓓ raining

MATCH.

1. SAT   Wednesday

2. MON   Thursday

3. THU   Tuesday

4. SUN   Saturday

5. WED   Friday

6. FRI   Sunday

7. TUE   Monday

Student's Name _____

Date _____

MATCH.

1. MAR   May

2. DEC   January

3. MAY   August

4. JUL   November

5. OCT   June

6. AUG   December

7. APR   February

8. NOV   October

9. JAN   March

10. JUN   September

11. SEP   July

12. FEB   April

Student's Name _____

Date _____

MON

1.
   March (A)   May (B)   Monday (C)   November (D)

SEP

2.
   Saturday (A)   Sunday (B)   December (C)   September (D)

JUN

3.
   January (A)   June (B)   Tuesday (C)   July (D)

THU

4.
   Fourth (A)   Tuesday (B)   Thursday (C)   Friday (D)

OCT

5.
   October (A)   August (B)   April (C)   November (D)

SUN

6.
   June (A)   Sunny (B)   Saturday (C)   Sunday (D)

Student's Name _____

Date _____

1. (A) penny
   (B) nickel
   (C) dime
   (D) quarter

2. (A) quarter
   (B) half dollar
   (C) dollar
   (D) nickel

3. (A) dime
   (B) dollar
   (C) penny
   (D) nickel

4. (A) dollar
   (B) half dollar
   (C) quarter
   (D) nickel

5. (A) nickel
   (B) quarter
   (C) dime
   (D) penny

6. (A) penny
   (B) half dollar
   (C) dollar bill
   (D) quarter

Foundations
Unit 4 Literacy Practice D (#4 of 4)

Student's Name _____

Date _____

MATCH.

1.

table

2.

refrigerator

3.

lamp

4.

rug

5.

chair

6.

bed

7.

sofa

Student's Name _____

Date _____

stove

1.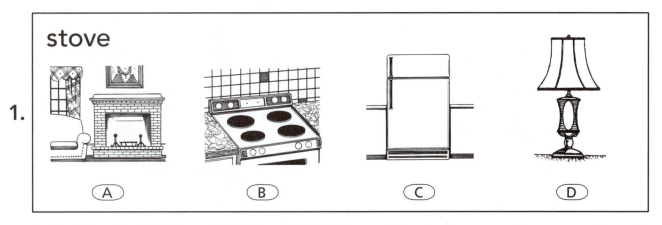

   A   B   C   D

closet

2.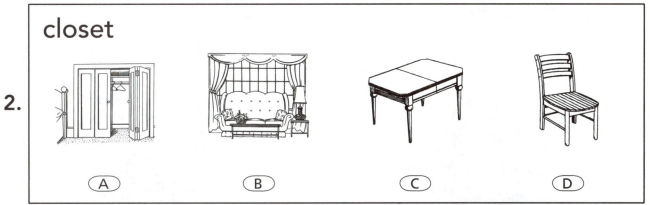

   A   B   C   D

sink

3.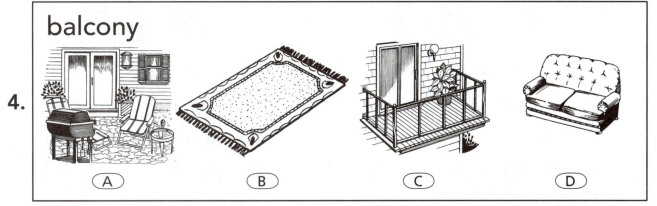

   A   B   C   D

balcony

4.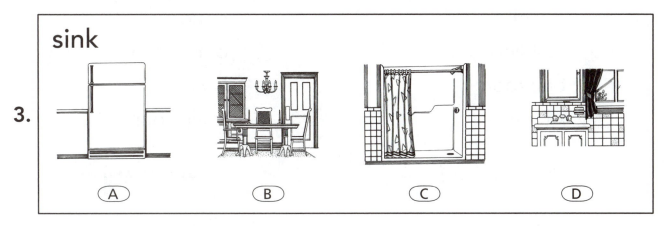

   A   B   C   D

Student's Name _____

Date _____

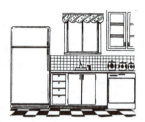

1.
- (A) bedroom
- (B) bathroom
- (C) dining room
- (D) kitchen

2.
- (A) bedroom
- (B) dining room
- (C) balcony
- (D) patio

3.
- (A) closet
- (B) building
- (C) bathroom
- (D) kitchen

4.
- (A) patio
- (B) dining room
- (C) kitchen
- (D) living room

5.
- (A) living room
- (B) shower
- (C) duplex
- (D) fireplace

6.
- (A) dormitory
- (B) balcony
- (C) table
- (D) patio

Student's Name _____

Date _____

MATCH.

 1.

 2.

 3.

 4.

 5.

 6.

 7.

 8.

supermarket

library

hospital

department store

gas station

laundromat

post office

bank

restaurant

1.

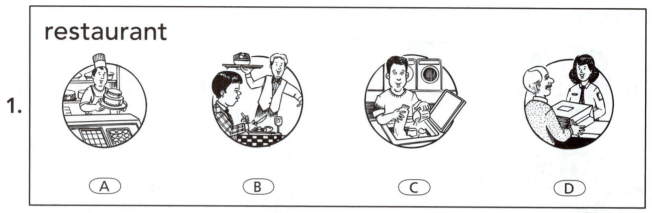

Ⓐ   Ⓑ   Ⓒ   Ⓓ

shopping mall

2.

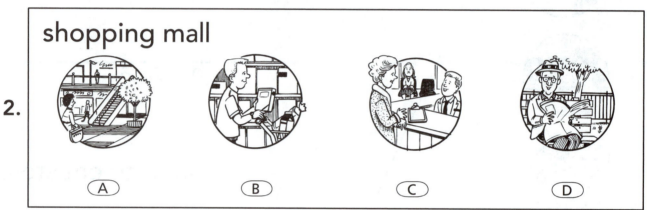

Ⓐ   Ⓑ   Ⓒ   Ⓓ

bus station

3.

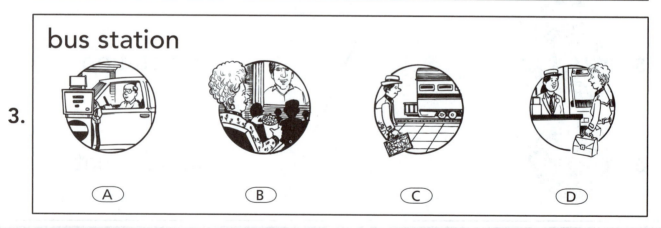

Ⓐ   Ⓑ   Ⓒ   Ⓓ

hospital

4.

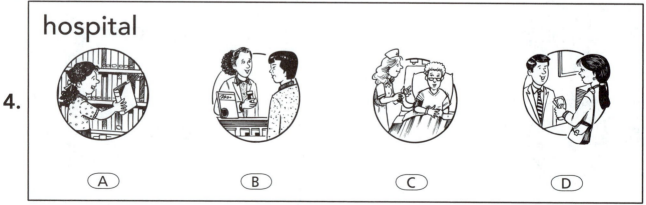

Ⓐ   Ⓑ   Ⓒ   Ⓓ

1.
- (A) bank
- (B) post office
- (C) grocery store
- (D) library

2.
- (A) laundromat
- (B) shopping mall
- (C) hospital
- (D) park

3.
- (A) bakery
- (B) restaurant
- (C) drug store
- (D) clinic

4.
- (A) supermarket
- (B) restaurant
- (C) hospital
- (D) movie theater

5.
- (A) laundromat
- (B) gas station
- (C) train station
- (D) bus station

6.
- (A) drug store
- (B) hospital
- (C) bakery
- (D) bank

Student's Name _____

Date _____

MATCH.

1.   sick

2.   hungry

3.   angry

4.   afraid

5.   sad

6.   thirsty

7.   tired

8.   happy

happy

1.

A   B   C   D

tired

2.

A   B   C   D

old

3.

A   B   C   D

average height

4.

A   B   C   D

Student's Name _____

Date _____

1.
- (A) angry
- (B) afraid
- (C) sick
- (D) happy

2.
- (A) hungry
- (B) thirsty
- (C) sad
- (D) tired

3.
- (A) tired
- (B) thirsty
- (C) angry
- (D) hungry

4.
- (A) tired
- (B) afraid
- (C) sick
- (D) sad

5.
- (A) short
- (B) tall
- (C) old
- (D) heavy

6.
- (A) heavy
- (B) short
- (C) average height
- (D) tall

MATCH.

 1.

 2.

 3.

 4.

 5.

 6.

 7.

 8.

apple

egg

cookie

tomato

banana

onion

potato

carrot

Student's Name _____

Date _____

bread

1.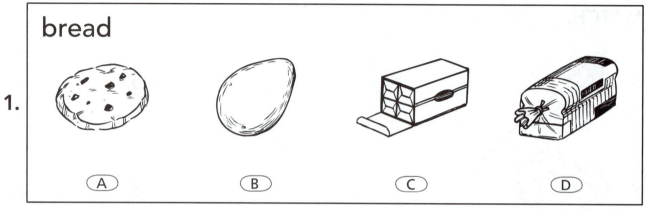

    Ⓐ   Ⓑ   Ⓒ   Ⓓ

milk

2.

    Ⓐ   Ⓑ   Ⓒ   Ⓓ

potato

3.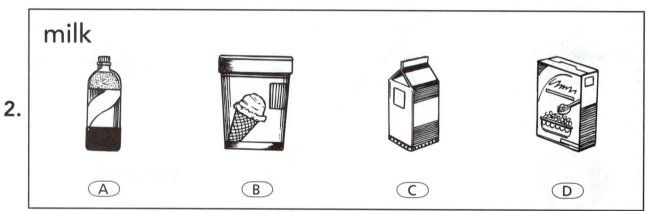

    Ⓐ   Ⓑ   Ⓒ   Ⓓ

cheese

4.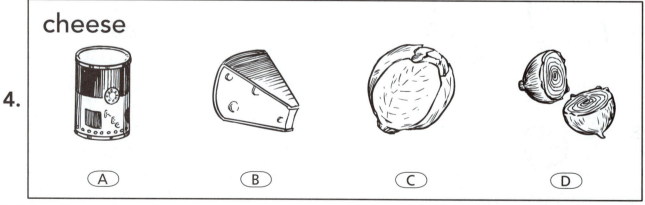

    Ⓐ   Ⓑ   Ⓒ   Ⓓ

Student's Name _____

Date _____

1. Ⓐ hot dog

    Ⓑ taco

    Ⓒ hamburger

    Ⓓ cereal

2. Ⓐ peach

    Ⓑ pizza

    Ⓒ potato

    Ⓓ taco

3. Ⓐ hamburger

    Ⓑ cheeseburger

    Ⓒ cheese

    Ⓓ sandwich

4. Ⓐ lemonade

    Ⓑ milk

    Ⓒ lettuce

    Ⓓ cereal

5. Ⓐ soda

    Ⓑ coffee

    Ⓒ milk

    Ⓓ ice cream

6. Ⓐ pizza

    Ⓑ sandwich

    Ⓒ taco

    Ⓓ hot dog

Student's Name _____

Date _____

MATCH.

1.   dress

2.   blouse

3.   necklace

4.   tie

5.   watch

6.   umbrella

7.   jacket

8.   suit

Student's Name _____

Date _____

belt

1.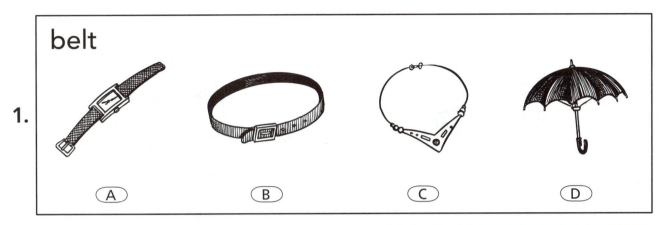

   A   B   C   D

pants

2.

   A   B   C   D

gloves

3.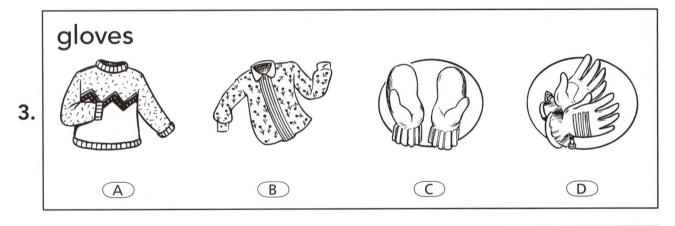

   A   B   C   D

shoes

4.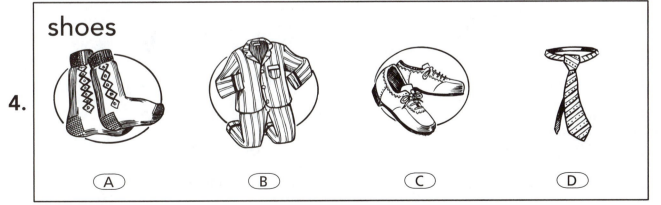

   A   B   C   D

Student's Name _____

Date _____

1. Ⓐ socks

    Ⓑ shirts

    Ⓒ suits

    Ⓓ shoes

2. Ⓐ shirt

    Ⓑ coat

    Ⓒ sweater

    Ⓓ jacket

3. Ⓐ blouse

    Ⓑ dress

    Ⓒ sweater

    Ⓓ coat

4. Ⓐ socks

    Ⓑ mittens

    Ⓒ gloves

    Ⓓ jeans

5. Ⓐ gloves

    Ⓑ pants

    Ⓒ pajamas

    Ⓓ suits

6. Ⓐ umbrella

    Ⓑ necklace

    Ⓒ watch

    Ⓓ belt

Student's Name _____

Date _____

MATCH.

1.    checkbook

2.   bank book

3.    package

4.    stamps

5.   money order

6.   air letter

7.    credit card

8.    check

Student's Name _____

Date _____

check

1.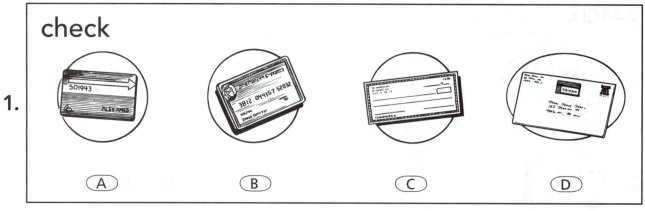

   (A)   (B)   (C)   (D)

bank book

2.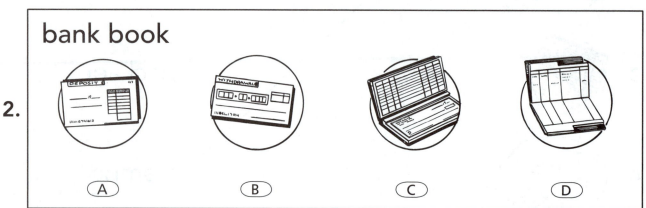

   (A)   (B)   (C)   (D)

air letter

3.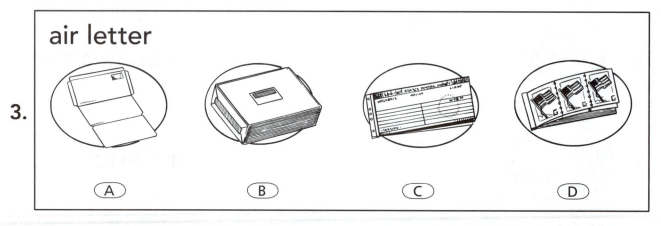

   (A)   (B)   (C)   (D)

deposit slip

4.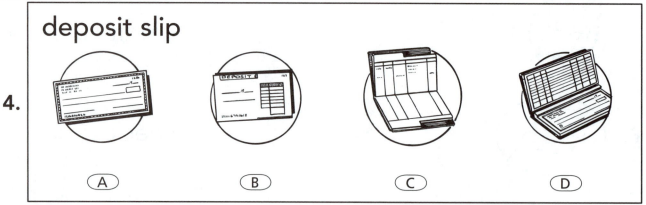

   (A)   (B)   (C)   (D)

1. (A) package
    (B) checkbook
    (C) bank book
    (D) money order

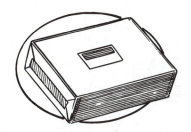

2. (A) air letter
    (B) registered letter
    (C) package
    (D) deposit slip

3. (A) money order
    (B) air letter
    (C) check
    (D) bank book

4. (A) check
    (B) credit card
    (C) deposit slip
    (D) withdrawal slip

5. (A) check
    (B) money order
    (C) air letter
    (D) withdrawal slip

6. (A) air letter
    (B) package
    (C) registered letter
    (D) stamp

Student's Name _____

Date _____

MATCH.

 1.　　　　　　　　　　　cough

 2.　　　　　　　　　　　backache

 3.　　　　　　　　　　　toothache

 4.　　　　　　　　　　　headache

 5.　　　　　　　　　　　cold

 6.　　　　　　　　　　　fever

 7.　　　　　　　　　　　stomachache

Student's Name _____

Date _____

1. earache

A   B   C   D

2. sore throat

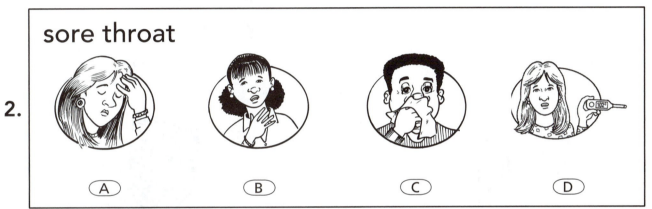

A   B   C   D

3. aspirin

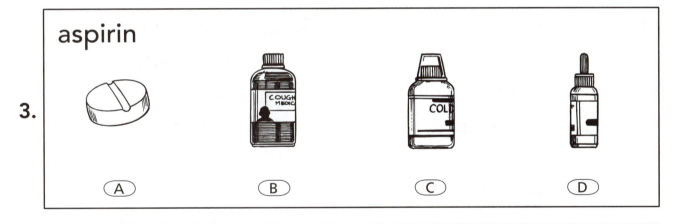

A   B   C   D

4. cough syrup

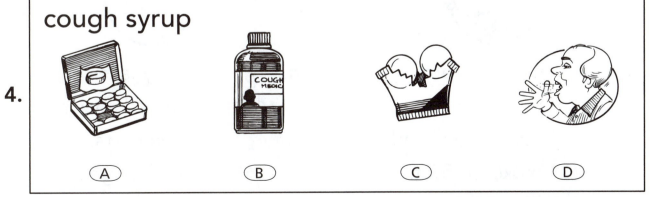

A   B   C   D

Student's Name _____

Date _____

1. (A) stomachache

    (B) backache

    (C) earache

    (D) headache

2. (A) fever

    (B) cold

    (C) cough

    (D) sore throat

3. (A) aspirin

    (B) antacid tablets

    (C) ear drops

    (D) cough syrup

4. (A) cold medicine

    (B) throat lozenges

    (C) cough syrup

    (D) aspirin

5. (A) I broke my arm.

    (B) I broke my leg.

    (C) I burned my hand.

    (D) I broke my foot.

6. (A) I cut my face.

    (B) I sprained my wrist.

    (C) My eye hurts.

    (D) I cut my finger.

Student's Name _____

Date _____

MATCH.

1. *L*   Z

2. *G*   f

3. *l*   G

4. *z*   n

5. *f*   L

6. *k*   I

7. *t*   k

8. *n*   t

Student's Name _____

Date _____

MATCH.

1. $\mathcal{A}$ j

2. $\mathcal{S}$ f

3. $\mathcal{J}$ a

4. $\mathcal{B}$ q

5. $\mathcal{D}$ b

6. $\mathcal{R}$ s

7. $\mathcal{Q}$ r

8. $\mathcal{F}$ d

Student's Name _____

Date _____

CIRCLE THE CORRECT LETTER.

1. *m*   N   M   W   U

2. *T*   I   Z   T   L

3. *E*   B   H   F   E

4. *f*   k   f   h   d

5. *h*   h   n   u   k

6. *z*   j   p   z   q

Student's Name _____

Date _____

CIRCLE THE CORRECT LETTER.

1. *E*   c   n   v   e

2. *G*   p   q   g   z

3. *H*   h   n   m   k

4. *i*   J   I   K   L

5. *m*   V   U   n   M

6. *q*   B   P   2   G

Student's Name _____

Date _____

MATCH.

1.    social studies

2. 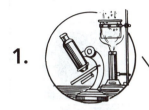   art

3.    technology

4.    English

5.    science

6.    music

7.    math

Student's Name _____

Date _____

art

1.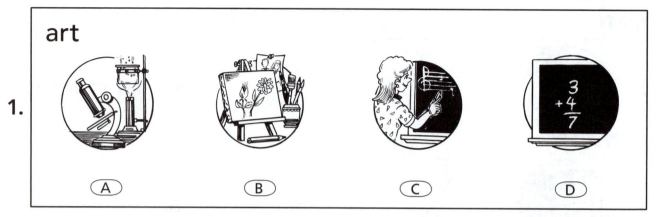

Ⓐ   Ⓑ   Ⓒ   Ⓓ

drama

2.

Ⓐ   Ⓑ   Ⓒ   Ⓓ

band

3.

Ⓐ   Ⓑ   Ⓒ   Ⓓ

football

4.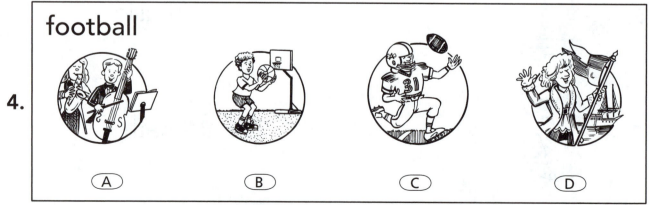

Ⓐ   Ⓑ   Ⓒ   Ⓓ

Student's Name _____

Date _____

1.
- Ⓐ principal
- Ⓑ school librarian
- Ⓒ school nurse
- Ⓓ teacher

2.
- Ⓐ school nurse
- Ⓑ custodian
- Ⓒ guidance counselor
- Ⓓ school librarian

3.
- Ⓐ guidance counselor
- Ⓑ English teacher
- Ⓒ P.E. teacher
- Ⓓ school librarian

4.
- Ⓐ auditorium
- Ⓑ custodian
- Ⓒ principal
- Ⓓ teacher

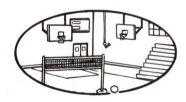

5.
- Ⓐ auditorium
- Ⓑ classroom
- Ⓒ office
- Ⓓ gym

6.
- Ⓐ principal's office
- Ⓑ cafeteria
- Ⓒ library
- Ⓓ gym

Student's Name _____

Date _____

MATCH.

 1.   electrician

 2.   repairperson

 3.   security guard

 4.   cook

 5.   gardener

 6.   cashier

 7.   delivery person

 8.   construction worker

Student's Name _____

Date _____

carpenter

1.

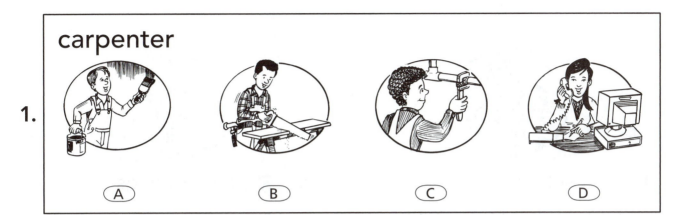

A   B   C   D

assembler

2.

A   B   C   D

doctor

3.

A   B   C   D

bus driver

4.

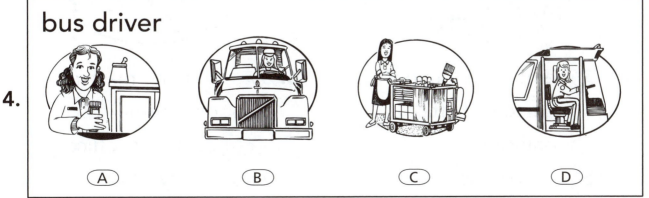

A   B   C   D

Student's Name _____

Date _____

1.
   (A) sell clothing
   (B) operate equipment
   (C) use a cash register
   (D) cook

2.
   (A) repair things
   (B) cook
   (C) sell watches
   (D) use a cash register

3.
   (A) clean buildings
   (B) use a cash register
   (C) assemble components
   (D) sell things

4.
   (A) cut hair
   (B) cook
   (C) repair things
   (D) sell clothing

5.
   (A) employee lounge
   (B) personnel office
   (C) bathroom
   (D) supply room

6.
   (A) vending machine
   (B) mailroom
   (C) personnel office
   (D) library

Student's Name _____

Date _____

MATCH.

1.   No right turn

2.    School nearby

3.   People in the street

4.    Stop

5.   No U-turn

6.   Train tracks ahead

7.   No left turn

Student's Name _____

Date _____

No left turn

School nearby

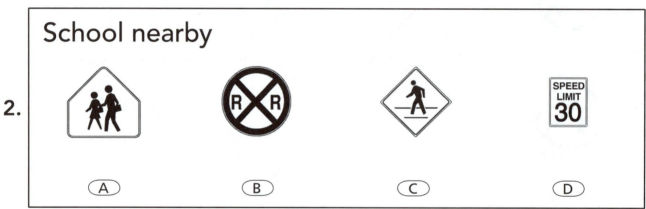

No U-turn

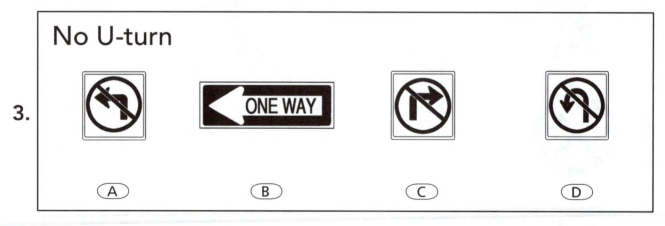

You can't go on this street.

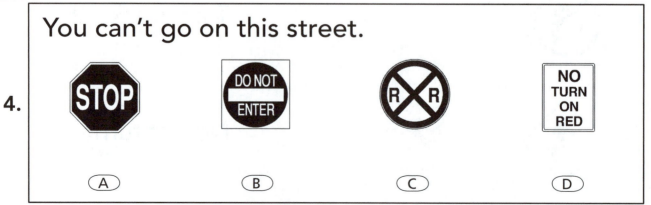

1. (A) No right turn.
   (B) No left turn.
   (C) No U-turn.
   (D) Slow down.

2. (A) School ahead.
   (B) Train tracks ahead.
   (C) Bus station ahead.
   (D) No right turn.

3. (A) Don't go that way.
   (B) Stop.
   (C) Slow down.
   (D) No left turn.

4. (A) Train tracks ahead.
   (B) School ahead.
   (C) People in the street.
   (D) Don't walk.

5. (A) No left turn.
   (B) No U-turn.
   (C) Stop.
   (D) No right turn.

6. (A) It's Bus Number 12.
   (B) It goes to the train station.
   (C) It's Train Number 2.
   (D) It's a train.

Student's Name _____

Date _____

MATCH.

1.

go swimming

2.

go jogging

3.

exercise

4.

go to a museum

5.

go to a concert

6.

see a movie

7.

go dancing

Student's Name _____

Date _____

1. play soccer

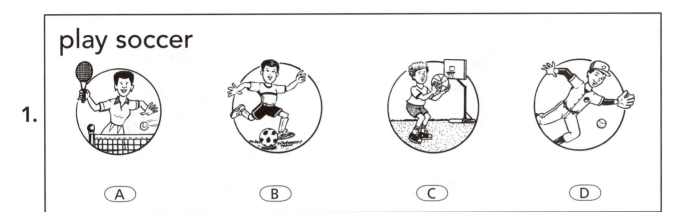

     (A)   (B)   (C)   (D)

2. go to the zoo

     (A)   (B)   (C)   (D)

3. go jogging

     (A)   (B)   (C)   (D)

4. go to a ballgame

     (A)   (B)   (C)   (D)

1. (A) play basketball
   (B) play tennis
   (C) play golf
   (D) play baseball

2. (A) listen to music
   (B) watch TV
   (C) go to a concert
   (D) exercise

3. (A) go to a museum
   (B) see a movie
   (C) see a play
   (D) go to the zoo

4. (A) go to a ballgame
   (B) go to the park
   (C) go dancing
   (D) go jogging

5. (A) play soccer
   (B) play tennis
   (C) play baseball
   (D) play golf

6. (A) go swimming
   (B) go dancing
   (C) go jogging
   (D) go rollerblading

FOUNDATIONS
BASIC READING INSTRUCTIONS & ANSWER KEY

Note to Teachers:

The *Foundations* Basic Reading Practice Worksheets are designed to provide students with systematic, explicit instruction in three fundamental reading skills:

• *Decoding*: the basic reading process of making connections between printed letters and the sounds they represent;

• *Letters, Words, Sentences*: the basic concept that letters make up words, words make up sentences, and spaces serve to separate these words;

• *Fluency*: the ability to read phrases and sentences aloud correctly with phrasing and expression that is appropriate for the meaning of the text and that demonstrates comprehension.

For each *Foundations* unit, there are three Basic Reading Practice Worksheets: Worksheet A focuses on decoding, Worksheet B offers practice with letters, words, and sentences, and Worksheet C develops students' fluency.

You can use these worksheets in a variety of ways depending on your students' needs, your class size and schedule, and whether there are tutors, aides, or other people available to work with students in small groups, pairs, or individually. Worksheets A and C are particularly suitable for individualized or small-group instruction with a tutor, an aide, or a more skilled student (using cross-ability grouping). The helping person can read a word or a line and have the student repeat. Or the student can try reading the word or line first, then listen to the helping person read it, and then repeat. If pairs of similar-ability students are working together, they can take turns reading and correcting each other. Worksheet B is appropriate for full-class practice since students can practice on their own and then go over the worksheets as a class, but students will benefit more if this worksheet is also used in individualized or small-group instruction.

Specific instructions:

Worksheet A: Students should hold their finger under each word as they read it aloud. If working with a partner or helper, an additional way to practice is for that person to say one of the words in a line in random order and have the student point to that word.

Worksheet B: Students should first silently scan the entire series of letters, visualize what words they make up, and then say the sentence aloud. They should then circle the letters that make up each word and say the sentence again. Finally, they should write the sentence on the line below, using proper spacing between each word.

Worksheet C: Students should first read the entire sentence silently and then read the sentence aloud with smooth pacing and phrasing. Early in this practice, it may be helpful to have students run their finger from left to right under the words as they read them. Later on, it will be better for students not to do this in order to promote greater fluency in their reading.

Since these may be among the first worksheets your students use in your instructional program, you can use these activities to introduce the basic concept of the top-to-bottom and left-to-right orientation of English text on a page.

Basic Reading Practice A Worksheets: Decoding
Contents

Answer Key

UNIT 14
1. stand
2. thank
3. stamp
4. blouse
5. cook
6. gray
7. drink
8. teach
9. jar
10. sprain

UNIT 15
1. hurt
2. right
3. are
4. go
5. cheese
6. red
7. comb
8. blue
9. four
10. eight

Basic Reading Practice B Worksheets: Letters, Words, Sentences
Answer Key

UNIT 1
1. My first name is Carlos.
2. My last name is Tran.
3. My address is 4 Center Street.
4. My apartment number is 2B.
5. Nice to meet you.

UNIT 2
1. Go to the board
2. Write your name.
3. Is this your pencil?
4. The map is on the wall.
5. There are books on my desk.

UNIT 3
1. I brush my teeth.
2. I go to work.
3. Every day I make dinner.
4. What are you doing?
5. My brother washes the dishes.

UNIT 4
1. What time is it?
2. I am in Apartment five.
3. My birthday is May tenth.
4. When do you go to school?
5. What floor do you live on?

UNIT 5
1. I live in an apartment building.
2. I cook in the kitchen.
3. My apartment has a nice living room.
4. There is a closet in the bedroom.
5. Where do you want this lamp?

UNIT 6
1. I am going to the bus station.
2. They are eating at a restaurant.
3. The school is next to the park.
4. The library is across from the clinic.
5. Is there a post office nearby?

UNIT 7
1. Our children are young.
2. She has blue eyes.
3. He has black hair and brown eyes.
4. What does he look like?
5. What language do you speak?

UNIT 8
1. Bananas are in Aisle Two.
2. Are there any apples?
3. Can I help you?
4. We need a loaf of bread.
5. Please get a pound of cheese.

UNIT 9
1. May I help you?
2. The pants are too short.
3. My favorite color is blue.
4. Coats are on the second floor.
5. What size shirt do you wear?

UNIT 10
1. I want to mail a package.
2. I put money in the bank.
3. I use my credit card in the store.
4. How much is a hamburger?
5. You can buy stamps at this window.

UNIT 11
1. She has a toothache.
2. My back hurts.
3. You should use cough syrup.
4. Where can I find cold medicine?
5. I want to make an appointment.

UNIT 12
1. The librarian is in the library.
2. My favorite subject is English.
3. I have soccer practice today.
4. I have English class third period.
5. What are you going to do today?

UNIT 13
1. I can fix cars.
2. A secretary can type.
3. He works at the hospital.
4. The mailroom is down the hall.
5. Put on your safety glasses!

UNIT 14
1. The bus station is on the right.
2. How do I get to the post office?
3. Take Bus Number Two to the library.
4. The laundromat is on Main Street.
5. There are train tracks ahead.

UNIT 15
1. I like to listen to music.
2. She works five days a week.
3. I went to the park yesterday.
4. What did you do yesterday?
5. What are you going to do tomorrow?

Read the words.

1. Dan	Jan	Nan	Van
2. Ben	Jen	Ken	Len
3. Bill	Gil	Jill	Will
4. Bob	Don	Jon	Ron
5. Bud	Judd	Gus	Russ

Circle the words. Write the sentences.

$\underline{My\ name\ is\ Anna.}$

1. MyfirstnameisCarlos.

_____

_ _ _ _ _ _ _ _ _ _ _ _ _ _

_____

2. MylastnameisTran.

_____

_ _ _ _ _ _ _ _ _ _ _ _ _ _

_____

3. Myaddressis4CenterStreet.

_____

_ _ _ _ _ _ _ _ _ _ _ _ _ _

_____

4. Myapartmentnumberis2B.

_____

_ _ _ _ _ _ _ _ _ _ _ _ _ _

_____

5. Nicetomeetyou.

_____

_ _ _ _ _ _ _ _ _ _ _ _ _ _

_____

Read the sentences.

1. My name is Anna.

2. My first name is Anna.

3. My last name is Ramos.

4. My name is Anna Ramos.

5. My address is 4 Main Street.

6. My apartment number is 2F.

7. My city is Los Angeles.

8. My zip code is 90036.

Student's Name _____

Date _____

Read the words.

1. pen   Ben   desk   pencil

2. map   sit   up   clock

3. name   take   erase   table

4. go   open   close   globe

5. ruler   student

Short & Long Vowels

Circle the words. Write the sentences.

Open your book.

1. Gototheboard.

2. Writeyourname.

3. Isthisyourpencil?

4. Themapisonthewall.

5. Therearebooksonmydesk.

Read the sentences.

1. The pen is on the desk.

2. The map is on the wall.

3. The pen is next to the pencil.

4. The ruler is on the table.

5. The globe is on the table.

6. The book is on the bookshelf.

7. This is my notebook.

8. Is this your notebook?

Student's Name _____

Date _____

Read the words.

1. get	bed	pen	desk
2. dinner	dishes	fifteen	fifty
3. hot	not	foggy	
4. brush	lunch	study	sunny
5. take	make	name	baby
6. feed	teeth	eat	read
7. go	home	cold	snow

Short & Long Vowels

Student's Name _____

Date _____

Circle the words. Write the sentences.

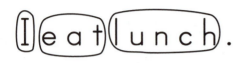

I eat lunch.

I eat lunch.

1. I brush my teeth.

2. I go to work.

3. Every day I make dinner.

4. What are you doing?

5. My brother washes the dishes.

Student's Name _____

Date _____

Read the sentences.

1. I get up.

2. I go to bed.

3. I make lunch.

4. I take a shower.

5. I feed the baby.

6. I'm feeding the baby.

7. I'm washing the dishes.

8. I'm making dinner.

Read the words.

1. map   hat   Pat   rat

2. name   date   take   cake

3. is   it   six   fifty

4. time   dime   nine   five

5. not   hot   Ron   Bob

6. home   hole   globe   close

Short & Long Vowels

Student's Name _____

Date _____

Circle the words. Write the sentences.

(What)(monthis)(it)?

~~What month is it?~~

1. Whattimeisit?

_____

2. IaminApartmentfive.

_____

3. MybirthdayisMaytenth.

_____

4. Whendoyougotoschool?

_____

5. Whatfloordoyouliveon?

_____

Student's Name _____

Date _____

Read the sentences.

1. What time is it?

2. What day is it?

3. What month is it?

4. What's today's date?

5. When is your birthday?

6. When do you go to work?

7. What floor do you live on?

8. What time does the train leave?

Read the words.

1. meet	feet	feed	teeth
2. see	three	street	sleep
3. eat	read	clean	speak
4. tea	please	leave	teacher
5. he	me	we	she
6. go	no	old	cold

Long Vowel Word Families

Circle the words. Write the sentences.

(Put) (it) (in) (the) (kitchen).

Put it in the kitchen.

1. Iliveinanapartmentbuilding.

2. Icookinthekitchen.

3. Myapartmenthasanicelivingroom.

4. Thereisaclosetinthebedroom.

5. Wheredoyouwantthislamp?

Student's Name _____

Date _____

Read the sentences.

1. The apartment has a nice bedroom.

2. The apartment has a very nice kitchen.

3. The apartment has a very small dining room.

4. There's a stove in the kitchen.

5. There's a shower in the bathroom.

6. Is there a closet in the bedroom?

7. There are four rooms in my apartment.

8. How many rooms are there in the apartment?

Read the words.

1. stand   stop   store

2. study   student   station

3. clean   clinic   close

4. globe   sleep   snow   speak

5. last   first   breakfast

6. hand   stand   second

7. lamp   desk   ask

Initial & Final Consonant Blends

Student's Name _____

Date _____

Circle the words. Write the sentences.

The bank is on Main Street.

1. Iamgoingtothebusstation.

2. Theyareeatingatarestaurant.

3. Theschoolisnexttothepark.

4. Thelibraryisacrossfromtheclinic.

5. Isthereapostofficenearby?

Student's Name _____

Date _____

Read the sentences.

1. I'm going to the bank.

2. I'm going to the drug store.

3. The post office is on Main Street.

4. The hospital is next to the park.

5. The library is across from the school.

6. The bank is between the school and the clinic.

7. Where are you going?

8. Is there a supermarket nearby?

Read the words.

1. black   blond   blue

2. bread   brown   broke

3. stand   stop   student

4. clean   clinic   close   globe

5. baby   study   penny   happy

6. thirsty   hungry   angry   laundry

7. bakery   grocery   library

**Initial Consonant Blends;
y as a Vowel**

Student's Name _____

Date _____

Circle the words. Write the sentences.

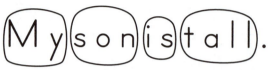 .

My son is tall.

1. Ourchildrenareyoung.

2. Shehasblueeyes.

3. Hehasblackhairandbrowneyes.

4. Whatdoeshelooklike?

5. Whatlanguagedoyouspeak?

Read the sentences.

1. She's young. He's old.

2. They're short. We're tall.

3. She has black hair.

4. He has blue eyes.

5. He's tall, with brown hair.

6. She's single. We're married.

7. I'm hungry. He's thirsty.

8. I'm from Mexico. I speak Spanish.

Student's Name _____

Date _____

Read the words.

1. short	shirt	shower	shopping
2. cheese	chair	check	Chinese
3. thin	think	thank	theater
4. dish	wash	brush	
5. bath	math	teeth	tenth
6. bank	thank	think	drink
7. apple	bottle	table	single

Initial & Final Consonant Digraphs;
Two-Syllable Words with Final *le*

Student's Name _____

Date _____

Circle the words. Write the sentences.

Milk is in Aisle One.

1. BananasareinAisleTwo.

- -

2. Arethereanyapples?

- -

3. CanIhelpyou?

- -

4. Weneedaloafofbread.

- -

5. Pleasegetapoundofcheese.

- -

Read the sentences.

1. I'm looking for a cookie.

2. We're looking for bread.

3. Is there any cheese?

4. Are there any eggs?

5. There isn't any more ice cream.

6. There aren't any more carrots.

7. Apples are in Aisle Four.

8. We need a bag of sugar.

Student's Name _____

Date _____

Read the words.

1. say	day	May	way
2. play	gray	away	Sunday
3. main	rain	pain	train
4. road	loaf	coat	boat
5. snow	slow	grow	crow
6. room	tooth	boot	school
7. you	soup	blue	glue

Vowel Digraphs

Circle the words. Write the sentences.

(Belts) (are) (over) (there).

Belts are over there.

1. MayIhelpyou?

2. Thepantsaretooshort.

3. Myfavoritecolorisblue.

4. Coatsareonthesecondfloor.

5. Whatsizeshirtdoyouwear?

Read the sentences.

1. I'm looking for a jacket.

2. I'm looking for a pair of jeans.

3. He's wearing a blue shirt and black pants.

4. The jacket is too large.

5. The blouse is too small.

6. Coats are on the first floor.

7. Watches are on the third floor.

8. What's the price of the dresses?

Read the words.

1.	jar	card	park	March
2.	first	shirt	skirt	thirsty
3.	hurt	turn	burn	church
4.	short	north	corn	fork
5.	house	blouse	pound	found
6.	how	brown	town	shower

Foundations
Unit 10 Basic Reading Practice A (#1 of 3)

R-Controlled Vowels;
Vowel Diphthongs

© 2007 Pearson Education, Inc.
Duplication for classroom use is permitted.

Student's Name _____

Date _____

Circle the words. Write the sentences.

I want to buy stamps.

1. Iwanttomailapackage.

2. Iputmoneyinthebank.

3. Iusemycreditcardinthestore.

4. Howmuchisahamburger?

5. Youcanbuystampsatthiswindow.

Student's Name _____

Date _____

Read the sentences.

1. Where's the bank book?

2. I use my ATM card every week.

3. I'm writing a check.

4. I want to send a letter.

5. I want to buy a money order.

6. You can buy stamps at the next window.

7. Your change is two dollars.

8. How much is a cheeseburger?

Read the words.

1. sore   more   store

2. four   your   pour

3. door   floor

4. book   cook   look   foot

5. put   push   pull

6. son   mother   brother   Monday

7. breakfast   sweater   head   bread

Circle the words. Write the sentences.

I have a headache.

I have a headache.

1. Shehasatoothache.

2. Mybackhurts.

3. Youshouldusecoughsyrup.

4. WherecanIfindcoldmedicine?

5. Iwanttomakeanappointment.

Student's Name _____

Date _____

Read the sentences.

1. I have a fever.

2. He has a sore throat.

3. She has an earache.

4. Where can I find aspirin?

5. Look in Aisle Five.

6. What should I do?

7. I think you should exercise.

8. Take one tablet three times a day.

Read the words.

1. is   his   has

2. use   these   those

3. nose   close   raise

4. cheese   please   excuse   closet

5. Chinese   Japanese   Vietnamese

Consonant *s = z*

Student's Name _____

Date _____

Circle the words. Write the sentences.

The teacher is in the classroom.

1. Thelibrarianisinthelibrary.

2. MyfavoritesubjectisEnglish.

3. Ihavesoccerpracticetoday.

4. IhaveEnglishclassthirdperiod.

5. Whatareyougoingtodotoday?

Read the sentences.

1. I'm going to the library.

2. They're going to the cafeteria.

3. She's my English teacher.

4. My favorite subject is math.

5. I have basketball practice after school today.

6. Our drama class is in the auditorium.

7. My English class is in Room Seventeen.

8. What are you going to do after school today?

Student's Name _____

Date _____

Read the words.

1. bedroom   bathroom   mailroom

2. football   basketball   baseball   ballgame

3. backache   toothache   stomachache

4. headache   earache

5. bookshelf   checkbook   fireplace

6. tablespoon   cheeseburger

7. repairperson   salesperson   housekeeper

Compound Words

Student's Name _____

Date _____

Circle the words. Write the sentences.

I can drive a taxi.

1. I c a n f i x c a r s .

2. A s e c r e t a r y c a n t y p e .

3. H e w o r k s a t t h e h o s p i t a l .

4. T h e m a i l r o o m i s d o w n t h e h a l l .

5. P u t o n y o u r s a f e t y g l a s s e s !

Read the sentences.

1. I'm a repairperson.

2. I can fix cars.

3. I'm looking for a job as a cook.

4. I'm an experienced truck driver.

5. I'm sure I can learn quickly.

6. What's your occupation?

7. I can't come to work today.

8. The supply room is down the hall.

Match.

1. hand		stamp
2. bank		gray
3. lamp		teach
4. house		cook
5. book		stand
6. play		sprain
7. think		jar
8. peach		thank
9. car		drink
10. train		blouse

Rhyming Words (Same Spelling)

Student's Name _____

Date _____

Circle the words. Write the sentences.

(The)(clinic)(is)(on)(the)(left).

The clinic is on the left.

1. Thebusstationisontheright.

_____

2. HowdoIgettothepostoffice?

_____

3. TakeBusNumberTwotothelibrary.

_____

4. ThelaundromatisonMainStreet.

_____

5. Therearetraintracksahead.

_____

Student's Name _____

Date _____

Read the sentences.

1. The hospital is on the left.

2. The bus station is on the right.

3. Take Bus Number 8 to the shopping mall.

4. Excuse me. How do I get to the airport?

5. Where do I get off for the main post office?

6. Slow down! You're driving too fast!

7. The sign says, "No Turn on Red."

8. The bus to Sacramento leaves at 4:00.

Match.

1. shirt		go
2. white		red
3. car		hurt
4. snow		eight
5. please		are
6. bread		comb
7. home		cheese
8. you		four
9. store		right
10. state		blue

Foundations
Unit 15 Basic Reading Practice A (#1 of 3)

Rhyming Words (Different Spelling)

Circle the words. Write the sentences.

I like to play soccer.

1. Iliketolistentomusic.

2. Sheworksfivedaysaweek.

3. Iwenttotheparkyesterday.

4. Whatdidyoudoyesterday?

5. Whatareyougoingtodotomorrow?

Read the sentences.

1. I like to play basketball.

2. He likes to go swimming.

3. I'm going to see a movie tomorrow.

4. She's going to go to a ballgame tomorrow.

5. I went to the zoo yesterday.

6. They saw a play yesterday.

7. What did you do yesterday?

8. What are you going to do tomorrow?

Foundations
Handwriting Practice

The *Foundations* Handwriting Practice Worksheets help learners master manuscript and cursive letter formation through tracing and copying activities correlated to each *Foundations* unit. Students should have some basic preliteracy concepts and skills before using these worksheets. (For students who do not yet have these skills, the *Foundations* Preliteracy Worksheets offer carefully-sequenced practice including how to hold a writing utensil—first to draw lines and shapes, then to learn the basic strokes that make up letters, and finally to develop handwriting skills to trace and copy upper case and lower case letters and numbers.)

The Handwriting Practice Worksheets provide writing practice with key vocabulary in each unit. In addition, the Unit 1 Worksheets offer practice with upper case and lower case manuscript letters, and the Unit 11 Worksheets offer practice with upper case and lower case cursive letters. Students make the transition from manuscript to cursive letters at Unit 11, thereby providing them with ample practice with the cursive form in the final five units of the program.

Student's Name _____

Date _____

READ. TRACE. COPY.

A A A A   a a a a

B B B B   b b b b

C C C C   c c c c

D D D D   d d d d

E E E E   e e e e

F F F F   f f f f

G G G G   g g g g

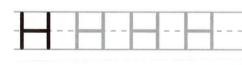

H H H H   h h h h

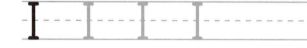

I I I I   i i i i

READ. TRACE. COPY.

J J J J   j j j j

K K K K   k k k k

L L L L   l l l l

M M M M   m m m m

N N N N   n n n n

O O O O   o o o o

P P P P   p p p p

Q Q Q Q   q q q q

R R R R   r r r r

Student's Name _____

Date _____

READ. TRACE. COPY.

S S S S   s s s s

T T T T   t t t t

U U U U   u u u u

V V V V   v v v v

W W W W   w w w w

X X X X   x x x x

Y Y Y Y   y y y y

Z Z Z Z   z z z z

READ. TRACE. COPY.

1. name   name

2. first   first

3. last   last

4. street   street

5. city   city

6. state   state

7. number   number

8. address   address

9. telephone   telephone

10. apartment   apartment

UNIT 2
Handwriting Practice

Student's Name _____

Date _____

READ. TRACE. COPY.

1. pen   pen

2. map   map

3. book   book

4. desk   desk

5. wall   wall

6. ruler   ruler

7. table   table

8. clock   clock

9. globe   globe

10. pencil   pencil

Student's Name _____

Date _____

READ. TRACE. COPY.

1. eat   eat

2. cook   cook

3. wash   wash

4. read   read

5. play   play

6. iron   iron

7. clean   clean

8. study   study

9. lunch   lunch

10. dinner   dinner

Student's Name _____

Date _____

READ. TRACE. COPY.

1. hot   hot

2. cold   cold

3. sunny   sunny

4. foggy   foggy

5. cloudy   cloudy

6. raining   raining

7. snowing   snowing

8. weather   weather

Student's Name _____

Date _____

READ. TRACE. COPY.

Sunday	Sunday	
Monday	Monday	
Tuesday	Tuesday	
Wednesday	Wednesday	
Thursday	Thursday	
Friday	Friday	
Saturday	Saturday	

Student's Name _____

Date _____

READ. TRACE. COPY.

January	January	
February	February	
March	March	
April	April	
May	May	
June	June	
July	July	
August	August	
September	September	
October	October	
November	November	
December	December	

READ. TRACE. COPY.

1. rug   rug   _____

2. bed   bed   _____

3. lamp   lamp   _____

4. chair   chair   _____

5. table   table   _____

6. stove   stove   _____

7. closet   closet   _____

8. shower   shower   _____

9. bedroom   bedroom   _____

10. bathroom   bathroom   _____

Student's Name _____

Date _____

READ. TRACE. COPY.

1. park   park
2. bank   bank
3. clinic   clinic
4. store   store
5. bakery   bakery
6. library   library
7. school   school
8. station   station
9. hospital   hospital
10. restaurant   restaurant

READ. TRACE. COPY.

1. old   old   _____

2. tall   tall   _____

3. hair   hair   _____

4. eyes   eyes   _____

5. short   short   _____

6. young   young   _____

7. single   single   _____

8. height   height   _____

9. hungry   hungry   _____

10. married   married   _____

Student's Name _____

Date _____

READ. TRACE. COPY.

1. milk   milk

2. taco   taco

3. soup   soup

4. onion   onion

5. bread   bread

6. apple   apple

7. orange   orange

8. potato   potato

9. lemonade   lemonade

10. sandwich   sandwich

Student's Name _____

Date _____

READ. TRACE. COPY.

1. coat   coat   _____

2. dress   dress   _____

3. shoes   shoes   _____

4. socks   socks   _____

5. blouse   blouse   _____

6. gloves   gloves   _____

7. umbrella   umbrella   _____

8. necklace   necklace   _____

9. sweater   sweater   _____

10. pajamas   pajamas   _____

READ. TRACE. COPY.

1. bank   bank   ....
2. check   check   ....
3. stamps   stamps   ....
4. letter   letter   ....
5. deposit   deposit   ....
6. address   address   ....
7. package   package   ....
8. envelope   envelope   ....
9. checkbook   checkbook   ....
10. withdrawal   withdrawal   ....

UNIT 11
Handwriting Practice A

Student's Name ______________________
Date ______________________

READ. TRACE. COPY.

A A A A   a a a a

B B B B   b b b b

C C C C   c c c c

D D D D   d d d d

E E E E   e e e e

F F F F   f f f f

G G G G   g g g g

H H H H   h h h h

I I I I   i i i i

Student's Name _____

Date _____

READ. TRACE. COPY.

J J J J   *j j j j*

K K K K   *k k k k*

L L L L   *l l l l*

m m m m   *m m m m*

n n n n   *n n n n*

O O O O   *o o o o*

P P P P   *p p p p*

2 2 2 2   *q q q q*

R R R R   *r r r r*

Student's Name _____

Date _____

READ. TRACE. COPY.

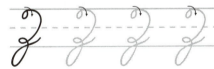

Student's Name _____

Date _____

READ. TRACE. COPY.

1. *arm*   *arm*

2. *eye*   *eye*

3. *foot*   *foot*

4. *head*   *head*

5. *neck*   *neck*

6. *fever*   *fever*

7. *cough*   *cough*

8. *finger*   *finger*

9. *stomach*   *stomach*

10. *headache*   *headache*

Student's Name _____

Date _____

READ. TRACE. COPY.

1. *art*   *art*

2. *math*   *math*

3. *drama*   *drama*

4. *soccer*   *soccer*

5. *library*   *library*

6. *science*   *science*

7. *football*   *football*

8. *English*   *English*

9. *orchestra*   *orchestra*

10. *cafeteria*   *cafeteria*

Student's Name _____

Date _____

READ. TRACE. COPY.

1. *cook*   *cook*

2. *baker*   *baker*

3. *doctor*   *doctor*

4. *cashier*   *cashier*

5. *painter*   *painter*

6. *plumber*   *plumber*

7. *teacher*   *teacher*

8. *waitress*   *waitress*

9. *mechanic*   *mechanic*

10. *carpenter*   *carpenter*

Student's Name _____

Date _____

READ. TRACE. COPY.

1. *bus* *bus*

2. *car* *car*

3. *map* *map*

4. *taxi* *taxi*

5. *walk* *walk*

6. *drive* *drive*

7. *train* *train*

8. *bicycle* *bicycle*

9. *subway* *subway*

10. *schedule* *schedule*

Student's Name _____

Date _____

READ. TRACE. COPY.

1. *zoo*   *zoo*

2. *park*   *park*

3. *play*   *play*

4. *movie*   *movie*

5. *music*   *music*

6. *tennis*   *tennis*

7. *soccer*   *soccer*

8. *concert*   *concert*

9. *museum*   *museum*

10. *ballgame*   *ballgame*

Foundations
Number Practice

The *Foundations* Number Practice Worksheets develop students' numeracy skills through carefully-sequenced practice coordinated with the content of each *Foundations* unit. The initial worksheets provide basic practice in recognizing, tracing, and copying numerals and the words representing numbers, while later worksheets offer life-skills-oriented practice with time, money, and other applications of number skills to everyday life situations.

Number Practice
Contents

Student's Name _____

Date _____

READ. TRACE. COPY.

0 0 0 0 -

1 1 1 1 -

2 2 2 2 -

3 3 3 3 -

4 4 4 4 -

5 5 5 5 -

6 6 6 6 -

7 7 7 7 -

8 8 8 8 -

9 9 9 9 -

Student's Name _____

Date _____

READ. TRACE. COPY.

1. one   one _____

2. two   two _____

3. three   three _____

4. four   four _____

5. five   five _____

6. six   six _____

7. seven   seven _____

8. eight   eight _____

9. nine   nine _____

10. ten   ten _____

MATCH.

1. three		10
2. nine		5
3. seven		8
4. two		3
5. ten		7
6. one		1
7. four		9
8. six		6
9. eight		2
10. five		4

Student's Name _____

Date _____

CIRCLE THE CORRECT NUMBER.

six

| 3 | 4 | (6) | 9 |

1. seven

| 2 | 7 | 5 | 1 |

2. three

| 0 | 2 | 8 | 3 |

3. five

| 5 | 1 | 9 | 7 |

4. nine

| 2 | 9 | 5 | 1 |

5. ten

| 0 | 1 | 5 | 10 |

UNIT 2
Number Practice A

Student's Name _____

Date _____

READ. TRACE. COPY.

11   11   11   11

12   12   12   12

13   13   13   13

14   14   14   14

15   15   15   15

16   16   16   16

17   17   17   17

18   18   18   18

19   19   19   19

Student's Name _____

Date _____

READ. TRACE. COPY.

1. eleven   eleven   _____

2. twelve   twelve   _____

3. thirteen   thirteen   _____

4. fourteen   fourteen   _____

5. fifteen   fifteen   _____

6. sixteen   sixteen   _____

7. seventeen   seventeen   _____

8. eighteen   eighteen   _____

9. nineteen   nineteen   _____

Student's Name _____

Date _____

MATCH.

1. twelve   11

2. nineteen   14

3. eleven   13

4. fifteen   12

5. fourteen   15

6. eighteen   19

7. sixteen   16

8. thirteen   17

9. seventeen   18

Student's Name _____

Date _____

CIRCLE THE CORRECT NUMBER.

fourteen			
5	15	4	(14)

1.
eleven			
1	11	13	15

2.
sixteen			
9	19	16	6

3.
twelve			
12	13	2	18

4.
eighteen			
13	8	18	3

5.
fifteen			
6	16	5	15

Student's Name _____

Date _____

READ. TRACE. COPY.

20 20 20 20 ------------------------------------

21 21 21 21 ------------------------------------

22 22 22 22 ------------------------------------

23 23 23 23 ------------------------------------

24 24 24 24 ------------------------------------

25 25 25 25 ------------------------------------

26 26 26 26 ------------------------------------

27 27 27 27 ------------------------------------

28 28 28 28 ------------------------------------

29 29 29 29 ------------------------------------

Student's Name _____

Date _____

READ. TRACE. COPY.

20 20 20 20

30 30 30 30

40 40 40 40

50 50 50 50

60 60 60 60

70 70 70 70

80 80 80 80

90 90 90 90

100 100 100

Student's Name _____

Date _____

READ. TRACE. COPY.

1. twenty   twenty

2. thirty   thirty

3. forty   forty

4. fifty   fifty

5. sixty   sixty

6. seventy   seventy

7. eighty   eighty

8. ninety   ninety

Student's Name _____

Date _____

CIRCLE THE CORRECT NUMBER.

1. | thirteen | 3 | (13) | 30 |

2. | six | 6 | 16 | 60 |

3. | seventy | 7 | 17 | 70 |

4. | nineteen | 9 | 19 | 90 |

5. | eight | 8 | 18 | 80 |

6. | fifty | 5 | 15 | 50 |

7. | fourteen | 4 | 14 | 40 |

8. | twelve | 2 | 12 | 20 |

9. | thirty | 3 | 13 | 30 |

Student's Name _____

Date _____

WRITE THE CORRECT NUMBER.

1. 1   2   3   4   5

2. 6   7   ____   9   10

3. 11   ____   13   14   15

4. 16   17   18   ____   20

5. 10   20   30   40   ____

6. 60   70   ____   90   100

7. 22   ____   24   25   26

8. 55   56   57   ____   59

9. 14   ____   16   17   18

Student's Name _____

Date _____

MATCH.

1.   10:45

2.   8:30

3.   2:15

4.   7:00

5.   7:30

6.   10:15

7.   5:00

8.   11:00

Student's Name _____

Date _____

4:00

1.

A   B   C   D

5:30

2.

A   B   C   D

4:45

3.

A   B   C   D

2:15

4.

A   B   C   D

Student's Name _____

Date _____

MATCH.

1.    50¢

2.   1¢

3.    10¢

4.   25¢

5. $1.00

6.    5¢

Student's Name _____

Date _____

10¢

1.

   A   B   C   D

5¢

2.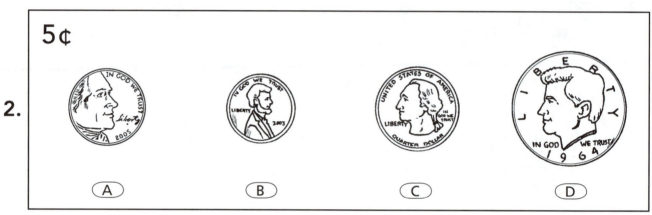

   A   B   C   D

25¢

3.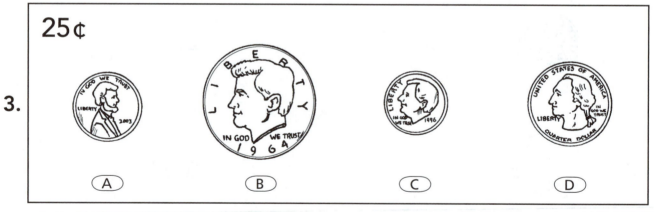

   A   B   C   D

1¢

4.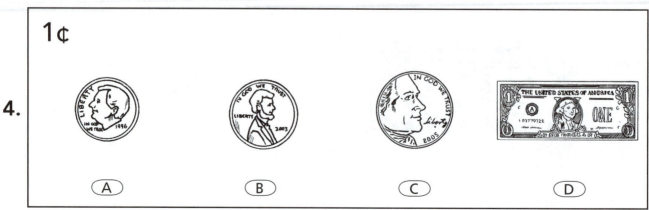

   A   B   C   D

Student's Name _____

Date _____

ORDINAL NUMBERS

Match.

1. 3rd   fifth

2. 15th   second

3. 1st   fifteenth

4. 5th   thirty-first

5. 50th   third

6. 2nd   twelfth

7. 12th   fiftieth

8. 31st   first

Student's Name _____

Date _____

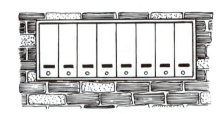

1. How many apartments are there in the building?

  (A) 6   (C) 8

  (B) 7   (D) 9

2. How many floors are there in the building?

  (A) 2   (C) 8

  (B) 4   (D) 16

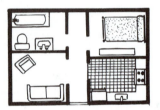

3. How many closets are there in the bedroom?

  (A) 1   (C) 3

  (B) 2   (D) 4

4. How many rooms are there in the apartment?

  (A) 1   (C) 5

  (B) 4   (D) 6

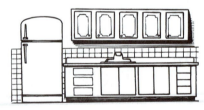

5. How many windows are there in the living room?

  (A) 2   (C) 6

  (B) 4   (D) 12

6. How many cabinets are there in the kitchen?

  (A) 1   (C) 4

  (B) 2   (D) 5

Student's Name _____

Date _____

What's your height?

1. 40 years old.   160 pounds.   5 feet 8 inches.
   (A)   (B)   (C)

What's your weight?

2. 155 pounds.   4 feet 11 inches.   22 years old.
   (A)   (B)   (C)

What's your age?

3. 5 feet 10 inches.   19 years old.   133 pounds.
   (A)   (B)   (C)

How tall are you?

4. 145 pounds.   6 feet.   27 years old.
   (A)   (B)   (C)

How old are you?

5. 5 feet 9 inches.   125 pounds.   18 years old.
   (A)   (B)   (C)

Student's Name _____

Date _____

one quart

1.   1 lb.   1 qt.   1 doz.
       (A)   (B)   (C)

two pounds

2.   2 qts.   1 lb.   2 lbs.
       (A)   (B)   (C)

a dozen eggs

3.   2 eggs   6 eggs   12 eggs
       (A)   (B)   (C)

half a pound

4.   1/2 lb.   1/2 qt.   1/2 doz.
       (A)   (B)   (C)

half a dozen

5.   1 doz.   1/2 doz.   1/2 lb.
       (A)   (B)   (C)

thirteen dollars and thirty cents

1.
$13.13
(A)
$30.30
(B)
$30.13
(C)
$13.30
(D)

seventy dollars and sixteen cents

2.
$17.16
(A)
$70.16
(B)
$70.60
(C)
$17.60
(D)

eight forty-five

3.
$80.45
(A)
$18.45
(B)
$8.45
(C)
$84.50
(D)

a dollar twenty

4.
$1.20
(A)
$20.00
(B)
$120.00
(C)
$20.20
(D)

forty ninety-nine

5.
$14.99
(A)
$40.99
(B)
$14.90
(C)
$40.90
(D)

Student's Name _____

Date _____

Write these checks. Write today's date, the name of the company, the dollar amounts in numbers and words, and sign your name.

1. Pay $470.00 to Central Hospital.

```
                                              142
                          _____ 20____

PAY TO THE
ORDER OF_____ $ [        ]

_____| dollars

FOR_____    _____
0 210000021 990 507931 0142
```

2. Pay $147.65 to Dominion Electric.

```
                                              143
                          _____ 20____

PAY TO THE
ORDER OF_____ $ [        ]

_____| dollars

FOR_____    _____
0 210000021 990 507931 0143
```

3. Pay $84.59 to Horizon Telephone.

```
                                              144
                          _____ 20____

PAY TO THE
ORDER OF_____ $ [        ]

_____| dollars

FOR_____    _____
0 210000021 990 507931 0144
```

Student's Name _____

Date _____

Take one pill three times a day.

1.

A

B

C

D

Take one tablet twice a day.

2.

A

B

C

D

Take one teaspoon four times a day.

3.

A

B

C

D

Take one capsule once a day.

4.

A

B

C

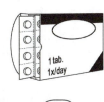
D

Student's Name _____

Date _____

Look at this student's class schedule. Answer the questions.

Period	Time	Class	Teacher	Room
1st	8:15–9:00	Math	Ms. Garcia	124
2nd	9:05–9:50	English	Mr. Fletcher	236
3rd	9:55–10:40	Science	Mrs. Wong	128
4th	10:45–11:30	Social Studies	Mr. Harris	312
5th	12:00–12:45	Art	Ms. Larsen	16
6th	12:50–1:35	Technology	Mrs. Ahmed	130
7th	1:40–2:25	Music	Mr. Ross	24

1. What class does this student have fifth period?

- (A) Math.
- (B) Science.
- (C) Art.
- (D) Technology.

2. Where is the Science class?

- (A) 4th period.
- (B) From 10:45 to 11:30.
- (C) Mrs. Wong.
- (D) In Room 128.

3. Which class is in Room 24?

- (A) Ms. Garcia's class.
- (B) The music class.
- (C) Mrs. Wong's class.
- (D) The art class.

4. It's 9:45. Where is this student now?

- (A) In Room 236.
- (B) In Room 128.
- (C) In Room 124.
- (D) In Room 312

5. How long is each period at this school?

- (A) 30 minutes.
- (B) 40 minutes.
- (C) 45 minutes.
- (D) One hour.

6. What time does this student probably eat lunch?

- (A) From 10:45 to 11:30.
- (B) From 11:30 to 12:00.
- (C) From 12:00 to 12:45.
- (D) From 12:45 to 12:50.

Student's Name _____

Date _____

Look at this paycheck and pay stub. Answer the questions.

Wilson's Department Store		Mercado, Y.		EMP. NO. 00427	
PAY PERIOD ENDING	**RATE**	**HOURS**		**GROSS PAY**	
10 05 09	13.00/hour	40		$520.00	
FED TAX 52.00				**GROSS PAY**	$520.00
FICA/MED 41.60				**DEDUCTIONS**	$144.10
STATE TAX 26.00					
HEALTH 24.50				**NET PAY**	$375.90

WILSON'S DEPARTMENT STORE   Check No.   4377291

Pay to **YOLANDA MERCADO**   Date Issued   10 08 09

THREE HUNDRED SEVENTY–FIVE DOLLARS AND NINETY CENTS ———— $375.90

Marjorie Denton

1. How much does this person make an hour?

   (A) $13.00
   (B) $40.00
   (C) $375.90
   (D) $520.00

2. How much does she pay for federal taxes?

   (A) $144.10
   (B) $375.90
   (C) $26.00
   (D) $52.00

3. How much are her total deductions?

   (A) $24.50
   (B) $144.10
   (C) $375.90
   (D) $520.00

4. How much does she take home after deductions?

   (A) $144.10
   (B) $375.90
   (C) $520.00
   (D) $1008.09

Student's Name _____

Date _____

Look at the bus schedule. Answer the questions.

Route 6B				
Day Street	Main Street	Pine Street	Fifth Avenue	Sixth Avenue
Weekdays				
5:45 AM	6:00	6:15	6:30	6:45
6:45	7:00	7:15	7:30	7:45
7:45	8:00	8:15	8:30	8:45
8:45	9:00	9:15	9:30	9:45
10:45	11:00	11:15	11:30	11:45
12:45 PM	1:00	1:15	1:30	1:45
1:45	2:00	2:15	2:30	2:45
3:45	4:00	4:15	4:30	4:45
4:45	5:00	5:15	5:30	5:45
5:45	6:00	6:15	6:30	6:45
6:45	7:00	7:15	7:30	7:45
8:45	9:00	9:15	9:30	9:45

1. How long does it take to go from Day Street to Main Street?

(A) 15 minutes.
(B) 30 minutes.
(C) 45 minutes.
(D) 60 minutes.

2. How long does it take to go from Main Street to Fifth Avenue?

(A) 15 minutes.
(B) 30 minutes.
(C) 45 minutes.
(D) 60 minutes.

3. It's 1:00 P.M. When will the next bus leave Fifth Avenue?

(A) 1:15 P.M.
(B) 1:30 P.M.
(C) 1:45 P.M.
(D) 2:00 P.M.

4. It's 8:00 P.M. When will the next bus leave Day Street?

(A) In 15 minutes.
(B) In 30 minutes.
(C) In 45 minutes.
(D) In an hour.

Student's Name _____

Date _____

MATCH.

1. January 14, 2009   2/9/99

2. November 21, 2008   5/8/93

3. May 8, 1993   12/3/11

4. September 2, 1999   1/14/09

5. August 5, 1993   3/12/11

6. March 12, 2011   9/2/99

7. December 3, 2011   11/21/08

8. February 9, 1999   8/5/93

Student's Name _____

Date _____

June 11, 2009

1. 9/6/11   11/9/06   11/6/09   6/11/09
    Ⓐ   Ⓑ   Ⓒ   Ⓓ

February 8, 1998

2. 8/2/98   2/8/98   8/19/98   2/19/98
    Ⓐ   Ⓑ   Ⓒ   Ⓓ

April 1, 2000

3. 1/4/00   4/1/20   4/1/00   1/4/20
    Ⓐ   Ⓑ   Ⓒ   Ⓓ

December 9, 2008

4. 9/8/12   9/12/08   12/8/09   12/9/08
    Ⓐ   Ⓑ   Ⓒ   Ⓓ

August 6, 1987

5. 8/6/87   6/19/87   6/8/87   8/19/87
    Ⓐ   Ⓑ   Ⓒ   Ⓓ

FOUNDATIONS
NUMBER PRACTICE ANSWER KEY

UNIT 1

Number Practice C
1. 3
2. 9
3. 7
4. 2
5. 10
6. 1
7. 4
8. 6
9. 8
10. 5

Number Practice D
1. 7
2. 3
3. 5
4. 9
5. 10

UNIT 2

Number Practice C
1. 12
2. 19
3. 11
4. 15
5. 14
6. 18
7. 16
8. 13
9. 17

Number Practice D
1. 11
2. 16
3. 12
4. 18
5. 15

UNIT 3

Number Practice D
1. 13
2. 6
3. 70
4. 19
5. 8
6. 50
7. 14
8. 12
9. 30

Number Practice E
1. 4
2. 8
3. 12
4. 19
5. 50
6. 80
7. 23
8. 58
9. 15

UNIT 4

Number Practice A
1. 5:00
2. 7:00
3. 8:30
4. 10:15
5. 10:45
6. 7:30
7. 11:00
8. 2:15

Number Practice B
1. B
2. A
3. D
4. C

Number Practice C
1. 25¢
2. 5¢
3. 50¢
4. 10¢
5. 1¢
6. $1.00

Number Practice D
1. D
2. A
3. D
4. B

UNIT 5

Number Practice
1. third
2. fifteenth
3. first
4. fifth
5. fiftieth
6. second
7. twelfth
8. thirty-first

UNIT 6

Number Practice
1. C
2. B
3. A
4. B
5. A
6. D

UNIT 7

Number Practice

1. C
2. A
3. B
4. B
5. C

UNIT 8

Number Practice

1. B
2. C
3. C
4. A
5. B

UNIT 9

Number Practice

1. D
2. B
3. C
4. A
5. B

UNIT 10

Number Practice

1. Correct date
   Central Hospital,
      $470.00
   Four hundred
      seventy dollars
      and 00/100
   Signature

2. Correct date
   Dominion Electric,
      $147.65
   One hundred forty-
      seven dollars and
      65/100
   Signature

3. Correct date
   Horizon Telephone,
      $84.59
   Eighty-four dollars
      and 59/100
   Signature

UNIT 11

Number Practice

1. C
2. D
3. B
4. A

UNIT 12

Number Practice

1. C
2. D
3. B
4. A
5. C
6. B

UNIT 13

Number Practice

1. A
2. D
3. B
4. B

UNIT 14

Number Practice

1. A
2. B
3. B
4. C

UNIT 15

Number Practice A

1. 1/14/09
2. 11/21/08
3. 5/8/93
4. 9/2/99
5. 8/5/93
6. 3/12/11
7. 12/3/11
8. 2/9/99

Number Practice B

1. D
2. B
3. C
4. D
5. A

Foundations
Vocabulary Practice

The *Foundations* Vocabulary Practice Worksheets review key unit vocabulary through a variety of exercise formats including word choice, sentence completion, and cloze reading. Students also practice common abbreviations and word categorization.

An Answer Key is provided on the pages following the Vocabulary Practice Worksheets.

A. Look at page 3 of *Foundations*. Write the missing word.

1. My _____ is Anna Ramos.

2. My _____ name is Anna.

3. My _____ name is Ramos.

4. My telephone _____ is (323) 456-8917.

5. My _____ is 4 Main Street.

6. My _____ number is 2F.

7. My _____ security number is 226-37-4189.

B. Look at page 12 of *Foundations*. Circle the correct word.

1. She's my (father   mother).

2. She's my (son   daughter).

3. He's my (mother   father).

4. She's my (grandmother   grandfather).

5. She's my (husband   wife).

6. He's my (brother   sister).

7. He's my (grandmother   grandfather).

8. She's my (granddaughter   grandson).

Student's Name _____

Date _____

A. Look at pages 18–19 of *Foundations*. Write the missing letters. Then say the words.

1. m__p

2. p__n

3. d__sk

4. cl__ck

5. n__tebook

6. gl__be

7. t__ble

8. r__ler

B. Look at page 26 of *Foundations*. Write the missing word.

1. Write your _____.

2. Open your _____.

3. Raise your _____.

4. Go to the _____.

5. Stand _____.

6. Sit _____.

7. _____ out your book.

8. _____ away your book.

UNIT 3
Vocabulary Practice

Student's Name _____

Date _____

A. Look at page 32 of *Foundations*. Write the missing word.

1. Every day I _____ my teeth.

2. Every day I _____ a shower.

3. I comb my _____ every day.

4. Every day I get up and eat _____.

5. I _____ to school every day.

6. I _____ TV every day.

7. I get undressed and go to _____.

B. Look at page 33 of *Foundations*. Write the missing word.

1. I _____ the dishes.

2. I _____ the laundry.

3. I _____ basketball.

4. I listen to _____.

5. I feed the _____.

6. I walk the _____.

7. I play the _____.

UNIT 4
Vocabulary Practice

Student's Name _____

Date _____

A. Look at page 53 of *Foundations*. Write the day.

1. FRI _____

2. SUN _____

3. TUE _____

4. SAT _____

5. MON _____

6. THU _____

7. WED _____

B. Look at page 57 of *Foundations*. Write the month.

1. MAR _____

2. JUN _____

3. AUG _____

4. JAN _____

5. NOV _____

6. SEP _____

7. MAY _____

8. FEB _____

9. APR _____

10. JUL _____

11. OCT _____

12. DEC _____

C. Write the correct month.

1. The second month of the year is _____.

2. The seventh month of the year is _____.

3. The third month of the year is _____.

4. The first month of the year is _____.

UNIT 5
Vocabulary Practice

Student's Name _____

Date _____

A. Look at pages 64–65 of *Foundations*. Write the missing letters. Then say the words.

1. b__d

2. r__g

3. b__throom

4. l__ving room

5. w__ndow

6. st__ve

7. s__fa

8. t__ble

9. f__replace

10. d__ning room

B. Look at page 75 of *Foundations*. Write the correct word.

1. There's a stove in the _____.

2. There's a bathtub in the _____.

3. A girl is studying in her _____.

4. There's a dog on the _____.

5. There's a TV in the _____.

C. Circle the correct word.

1. I live in a nice apartment (floor   building).

2. There's a (shower   sofa) in my bathroom.

3. There's a new (bathtub   refrigerator) in our kitchen.

4. Please put the table in the (dining room   fireplace).

UNIT 6
Vocabulary Practice

Student's Name _____

Date _____

A. Look at pages 76–77 of *Foundations*. Write the missing word.

1. bus _____

4. grocery _____

2. post _____

5. gas _____

3. shopping _____

6. movie _____

B. Look at page 87 of *Foundations*. Write the correct word.

1. A man is buying stamps at the _____.

2. A woman is reading a book in the _____.

3. A man is buying medicine in the _____.

4. A woman is washing her clothes at the _____.

5. A woman is in her car at the _____.

6. A man and a woman are eating at a _____.

7. A woman and a man are buying food at the _____.

8. Children are playing basketball in the _____.

9. A man is putting money in the _____.

Student's Name _____

Date _____

A. Match the opposites.

1. young   married

2. short   happy

3. thin   old

4. sad   heavy

5. single   tall

B. Circle the correct word.

1. He has (angry   curly) hair.

2. My daughter has blond (hair   eyes).

3. She isn't tall or short. She's average (weight   height).

4. I go to the clinic when I'm (sick   tired).

5. He speaks (Mexico   Spanish).

6. She speaks (Brazil   Portuguese).

7. I'm from (China   Chinese).

8. Where are you (speak   from)?

9. What (language   country) do you speak?

10. I'm not young or old. I'm (average height   middle-aged).

A. Write these words in the correct categories.

apple	butter	donut	onion
banana	cheese	lettuce	orange
bread	cookie	milk	potato

Fruits

_____

_____

_____

Vegetables

_____

_____

_____

Baked Goods

_____

_____

_____

Dairy

_____

_____

_____

B. Circle the correct word.

1. We need a bunch of (milk   bananas).

2. We need a (loaf   quart) of bread.

3. Please get a dozen (cereal   eggs).

4. Please get a (bag   jar) of sugar.

5. I'm thirsty. I'd like (mayonnaise   lemonade), please.

Student's Name _____

Date _____

A. Write these words in the correct categories.

black	large	small
blouse	medium	sweater
brown	shirt	white

Clothing   **Colors**

_____   _____

_____   _____

_____   _____

Sizes

_____

_____

_____

B. Circle the correct word.

1. I'm looking for a pair of (pants   necklace).

2. My favorite color is (belt   blue).

3. This coat is too (small   size).

4. What size shirt do you (matter   wear)?

5. What's the (medium   price) of the shoes?

UNIT 10
Vocabulary Practice

Student's Name _____

Date _____

A. Look at pages 132–133 of *Foundations*. Write the missing word.

1. deposit _____

4. bank _____

2. return _____

5. money _____

3. credit _____

6. post _____

B. Look at page 143 of *Foundations*. Read the story and circle the correct words.

A woman is putting money in the bank. She has her bank book, a check,

and a | deposit   withdrawal |^1 slip. A woman is getting money at the

| checkbook   ATM |^2.

At the post office, the man on the left is buying | coins   stamps |^3.

A woman is mailing a | package   air letter |^4. The man on the right

is buying a | credit card   money order |^5.

At the supermarket, the woman on the left is writing a

| deposit   check |^6. The woman in the middle is buying food with her

| credit card   envelope |^7. The man on the right is paying with a twenty-

dollar bill. His | return   change |^8 is $2.50.

Student's Name _____

Date _____

A. Look at pages 144–145 of *Foundations*. Unscramble the words.

1. gle _____   **5.** dolc _____

2. mar _____   **6.** reevf _____

3. tofo _____   **7.** hugco _____

4. kenc _____   **8.** gernif _____

B. Circle the correct word.

1. My (stomach   stomachache) hurts.

2. I have a sore (cough   throat).

3. When I have an earache, I use ear (drops   syrup).

4. Excuse me. Where can I find throat (medicine   lozenges)?

5. Hello. I want to (come in   make) an appointment.

6. I think you should take one (vitamin   meal) every day.

7. You should (eat   sleep) eight hours every night.

8. My son just fell! Please send (a checkup   an ambulance)!

9. Cold medicine is in (Aisle   Doctor) Three.

10. What's the (hurt   matter)?

Student's Name _____

Date _____

A. Look at pages 158–159 of *Foundations*. Write these words in the correct categories.

band	custodian	math	science
cafeteria	English	office	soccer
choir	library	principal	teacher

People at School

_____

_____

_____

School Subjects

_____

_____

_____

Places at School

_____

_____

_____

School Activities

_____

_____

_____

B. Circle the correct word.

1. My favorite subject is (auditorium   science).

2. I have (football   guidance) practice after school today.

3. My head hurts. I'm going to the (principal's   nurse's) office.

4. Basketball practice is in the (cafeteria   gym).

5. Ms. Bryant is the new (librarian   library).

Student's Name _____

Date _____

A. Look at pages 170–171 of *Foundations*. Unscramble the words.

1. koco _____

2. rabek _____

3. troodc _____

4. rebrab _____

5. nicemach _____

6. ternaip _____

7. drrenarg _____

8. creeyarts _____

B. Circle the correct words.

1. I'm looking for a job as a (cash register   cashier).

2. I can (drive   driver) a truck.

3. I'm an experienced (type   secretary).

4. What can you do? Tell me about your (job skills   want ads).

5. He's a (salesperson   waiter) in a restaurant.

6. Fill out the job (application   occupation).

7. I can't come to work today. I'm (the matter   sick).

8. The personnel office is across from the supply (lounge   room).

9. Put on your (safety glasses   wet floor).

10. Carlos works six (months   days) a week.

Student's Name _____

Date _____

A. Write these words in the correct categories.

airport	bicycle	clinic	subway
bank	bus	library	taxi
	car	park	

Transportation   **Places in the Community**

_____   _____

_____   _____

_____   _____

_____   _____

                                 _____

B. Look at page 189 of *Foundations*. Write the missing word.

1. No Right _____   4. _____ Way

2. Do Not _____   5. _____ Limit

3. No Turn on _____   6. _____ U-Turn

C. Circle the correct word.

1. I (ride   drive) a bicycle to work.

2. The clinic is on the (next   left).

3. The (sign   stop) says, "Do Not Enter."

4. The next bus is at 6:30. It's on the bus (number   schedule).

Student's Name _____

Date _____

A. Match.

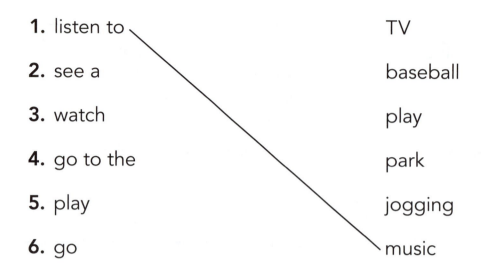

1. listen to   TV

2. see a   baseball

3. watch   play

4. go to the   park

5. play   jogging

6. go   music

B. Write these words in the correct categories.

baseball	golf	play	tennis
concert	movie	soccer	TV
	music	swimming	

Sports	**Entertainment**
_____	_____
_____	_____
_____	_____
_____	_____

FOUNDATIONS
VOCABULARY PRACTICE ANSWER KEY

UNIT 1
Vocabulary Practice

A.
1. name
2. first
3. last
4. number
5. address
6. apartment
7. social

B.
1. mother
2. daughter
3. father
4. grandmother
5. wife
6. brother
7. grandfather
8. granddaughter

UNIT 2
Vocabulary Practice

A.
1. m<u>a</u>p
2. p<u>e</u>n
3. d<u>e</u>sk
4. cl<u>o</u>ck
5. n<u>o</u>tebook
6. gl<u>o</u>be
7. t<u>a</u>ble
8. r<u>u</u>ler

B.
1. name
2. book
3. hand
4. board
5. up
6. down
7. Take
8. Put

UNIT 3
Vocabulary Practice

A.
1. brush
2. take
3. hair
4. breakfast
5. go
6. watch
7. bed

B.
1. wash
2. do
3. play
4. music
5. baby
6. dog
7. guitar

UNIT 4
Vocabulary Practice

A.
1. Friday
2. Sunday
3. Tuesday
4. Saturday
5. Monday
6. Thursday
7. Wednesday

B.
1. March
2. June
3. August
4. January
5. November
6. September
7. May
8. February
9. April
10. July
11. October
12. December

C.
1. February
2. July
3. March
4. January

UNIT 5
Vocabulary Practice

A.
1. bed
2. rug
3. bathroom
4. living room
5. window
6. stove
7. sofa
8. table
9. fireplace
10. dining room

B.
1. kitchen
2. bathroom
3. bedroom
4. patio
5. living room

C.
1. building
2. shower
3. refrigerator
4. dining room

UNIT 6
Vocabulary Practice

A.
1. station
2. office
3. mall
4. store
5. station
6. theater

B.
1. post office
2. park
3. drug store
4. laundromat
5. gas station
6. restaurant
7. supermarket
8. park
9. bank

UNIT 7
Vocabulary Practice

A.
1. old
2. tall
3. heavy
4. happy
5. married

B.
1. curly
2. hair
3. height
4. sick
5. Spanish
6. Portuguese
7. China
8. from
9. language
10. middle-aged

UNIT 8
Vocabulary Practice

A. *(Order of answers can vary.)*
Fruits: apple, banana, orange
Vegetables: lettuce, onion, potato
Baked Goods: bread, cookie, donut
Dairy: butter, cheese, milk

B.
1. bananas
2. loaf
3. eggs
4. bag
5. lemonade

UNIT 9
Vocabulary Practice

A. *(Order of answers can vary.)*
Clothing: blouse, shirt, sweater
Colors: black, brown, white
Sizes: large, medium, small

B.
1. pants
2. blue
3. small
4. wear
5. price

UNIT 10
Vocabulary Practice

A.
1. slip
2. address
3. card
4. book
5. order
6. office

B.
1. deposit
2. ATM
3. stamps
4. package
5. money order
6. check
7. credit card
8. change

UNIT 11
Vocabulary Practice

A.
1. leg
2. arm
3. foot
4. neck
5. cold
6. fever
7. cough
8. finger

B.
1. stomach
2. throat
3. drops
4. lozenges
5. make
6. vitamin
7. sleep
8. an ambulance
9. Aisle
10. matter

UNIT 12
Vocabulary Practice

A. *(Order of answers can vary.)*
People at School: custodian, principal, teacher
School Subjects: English, math, science
Places at School: cafeteria, library, office
School Activities: band, choir, soccer

B.
1. science
2. football
3. nurse's
4. gym
5. librarian

UNIT 13
Vocabulary Practice

A.
1. cook
2. baker
3. doctor
4. barber
5. mechanic
6. painter
7. gardener
8. secretary

B.
1. cashier
2. drive
3. secretary
4. job skills
5. waiter
6. application
7. sick
8. room
9. safety glasses
10. days

UNIT 14
Vocabulary Practice

A. *(Order of answers can vary.)*
Transportation: bicycle, bus, car, subway, taxi
Places in the Community: airport, bank, clinic, library, park

B.
1. Turn
2. Enter
3. Red
4. One
5. Speed
6. No

C.
1. ride
2. left
3. sign
4. schedule

UNIT 15
Vocabulary Practice

A.
1. music
2. play
3. TV
4. park
5. baseball
6. jogging

B. *(Order of answers can vary.)*
Sports: baseball, golf, soccer, swimming, tennis
Entertainment: concert, movie, music, play, TV

Foundations
Classroom Labels

The *Foundations* Classroom Labels provide large-print signs that can be posted next to key classroom objects and furnishings. While most of the vocabulary relates to Unit 2, it will be useful to have these signs posted in the classroom from the first day of instruction.

board

book

bookshelf

bulletin board

calculator

chair

chalk

clock

computer

desk

door

eraser

globe

map

notebook

overhead projector

pen

pencil

ruler

screen

student

table

teacher

TV

wall

window

Foundations
Unit Flash Cards

The *Foundations* Unit Flash Cards provide an economical study tool for students. You can reproduce and cut up each unit's cards to offer students their own set of flash cards for individual practice as well as for classroom activities and games. The flash cards are especially useful for playing Lotto and other matching games in conjunction with the *Foundations* Vocabulary Photo Cards.

name	first name
last name	address
apartment number	city
state	zip code

telephone number	cell phone number
e-mail address	social security number
wife	husband
mother	father

| daughter | son |
| grandmother | grandfather |

| sister | brother |

| grandmother | grandfather |

| aunt | uncle |

niece

nephew

cousin

granddaughter

grandson

pen

pencil

book

notebook

ruler

eraser

calculator

bookshelf

desk	board
chalk	map
globe	TV
computer	bulletin board

overhead projector	table
chair	clock
screen	student
teacher	wall

Stand up.

Go to the board.

Write your name.

Erase your name.

Sit down.

Take out your book.

Open your book.

Raise your hand.

Close your book.

Put away your book.

Point to the clock.

get up	take a shower
brush my teeth	comb my hair
get dressed	eat breakfast
go to work	eat lunch

go to school	come home
cook dinner	read
watch TV	get undressed
go to bed	

make breakfast	make lunch
make dinner	clean
wash the dishes	do the laundry
iron	feed the baby

walk the dog	study
exercise	listen to music
play the guitar	play basketball

sunny	cloudy
hot	cold
raining	snowing
foggy	

Sunday	Monday
Tuesday	Wednesday
Thursday	Friday
Saturday	

January	February
March	April
May	June
July	August

September	October
November	**December**
penny	nickel
dime	quarter

half dollar

dollar bill

five-dollar bill

ten-dollar bill

twenty-dollar bill

house	apartment building
living room	kitchen
bedroom	bathroom
dining room	balcony

patio	refrigerator
shower	closet
fireplace	stove
window	bathtub

table	sofa
bed	chair
rug	lamp
cabinet	

laundromat	bank
clinic	bakery
library	gas station
bus station	drug store

grocery store	post office
supermarket	hospital
park	restaurant
shopping mall	movie theater

train station	department store
on	next to
across from	between

young	middle-aged
old	tall
average height	short
thin	average weight

heavy	single
married	divorced
widowed	hair
eyes	black

blond	brown
gray	red
white	blue
green	

afraid	angry
happy	hungry
sad	sick
thirsty	tired

cookie	banana
carrot	tomato
potato	peach
apple	orange

egg	onion
bread	cheese
milk	cereal
butter	sugar

lettuce	soup
soda	ice cream
a box of cookies	a bunch of bananas
a jar of mayonnaise	a dozen eggs

hamburger	hot dog
sandwich	cheeseburger
taco	pizza
donut	lemonade

coffee

tea

box

bag

can

loaf

bunch

bottle

pound	jar
quart	dozen
half a pound	half a dozen

shirt	coat
suit	belt
jacket	tie
sweater	umbrella

| blouse | dress |
| skirt | shoes |

| watch | necklace |

| skirt | shoes |

| pants | socks |

jeans	gloves
mittens	pajamas
red	pink
orange	yellow

green	blue
purple	black
white	gray
brown	

small

medium

large

extra-large

size

price

bank book	ATM card
deposit slip	withdrawal slip
check	checkbook
credit card	bank

stamps	package
registered letter	money order
air letter	post office
envelope	

head	eye
ear	nose
neck	back
stomach	arm

hand	finger
leg	foot
backache	cold
cough	earache

fever	headache
sore throat	stomachache
toothache	cough syrup
aspirin	ear drops

cold
medicine

antacid
tablets

throat
lozenges

broke
my arm

broke my leg

burned my
hand

cut my face

cut my finger

sprained my wrist	pill
tablet	capsule
caplet	teaspoon
tablespoon	

English teacher	principal
school nurse	P.E. teacher
guidance counselor	custodian
school librarian	

auditorium

cafeteria

gym

library

office

principal's office

nurse's office

guidance office

math

English

social studies

science

art

music

technology

band	orchestra
choir	drama
football	soccer
basketball	

cook	custodian
gardener	cashier
electrician	repairperson
delivery person	security guard

police officer	construction worker
bus driver	painter
teacher	baker
secretary	taxi driver

truck driver	plumber
mechanic	carpenter
waitress	waiter
housekeeper	assembler

doctor

salesperson

pharmacist

barber

assemble components	cook
sell clothing	cut hair
repair watches	operate equipment
use a cash register	

supply room	cafeteria
mailroom	bathroom
employee lounge	personnel office
vending machine	

walk	drive a car
ride a bicycle	take a bus
take a subway	take a taxi
bus schedule	map

Do Not Enter	No Left Turn
No Right Turn	No Turn on Red
No U-Turn	One Way
Speed Limit	Stop

play soccer	play basketball
play tennis	watch TV
listen to music	exercise
go jogging	go swimming

go rollerblading	go dancing
see a movie	go to the park
see a play	go to a concert
play baseball	play golf

go to
a ballgame

go to
a museum

go to the zoo

Foundations
Activity Masters

The activity masters include ready-to-use word cards and activity sheets for the multilevel activities and games suggested throughout the *Foundations* Teacher's Guide.

A	B	C
D	E	F
G	H	I
J	K	L
M	N	O

P | Q | R

S | T | U

V | W | X

Y | Z |

a b c

d e f

g h i

j k l

m	n	o
p	q	r
s	t	u
v	w	x
y	z	

0	1	2
3	4	5
6	7	8
9	10	

zero	one	two
three	four	five
six	seven	eight
nine	ten	

pen	pencil	book
notebook	ruler	eraser
calculator		

bookshelf	desk	board
chalk	map	globe
TV	computer	bulletin board
overhead projector	table	

Stand up.	Go to the board.	Write your name.
Erase your name.	Sit down.	Take out your book.
Open your book.	Raise your hand.	Close your book.
Put away your book.		

11	**12**	**13**
14	**15**	**16**
17	**18**	**19**

For *Foundations* Teacher's Guide
Page 34, Activities 3, 4
Page 57, Activity 1
Page 58, Activity 2

eleven	twelve	thirteen
fourteen	fifteen	sixteen
seventeen	eighteen	nineteen

get up	take a shower	brush my teeth
comb my hair	get dressed	eat breakfast
go to work	eat lunch	go to school
come home	cook dinner	read
watch TV	get undressed	go to bed

get	up
take	a shower
brush	my teeth
comb	my hair
get	dressed
eat	breakfast
go	to work
eat	lunch
go	to school
come	home
cook	dinner
watch	TV
get	undressed
go	to bed

making breakfast	making lunch	making dinner
cleaning	washing the dishes	doing the laundry
ironing	feeding the baby	walking the dog
studying	exercising	listening to music
playing the guitar	playing basketball	

making	breakfast
making	lunch
making	dinner
washing	the dishes
doing	the laundry
feeding	the baby
walking	the dog
listening	to music
playing	the guitar
playing	basketball
cleaning	the house

every day - my mother - go - to work

every day - I - comb - my hair

every day - my grandson - exercise

every day - my sister - wash - the dishes

every day - my father - take - a shower

right now - I - make - lunch

right now - I - listen to - music

right now - I - clean - the house

right now - I - do - the laundry

right now - I - study - English

sunny	cloudy	hot
cold	raining	snowing
foggy		

20	30	40
50	60	70
80	90	100

For *Foundations* Teacher's Guide
Page 51, Activities 3, 4
Page 57, Activity 1
Page 58, Activity 2

18

©2007 Pearson Education, Inc.
Duplication for classroom use is permitted.

twenty	thirty	forty
fifty	sixty	seventy
eighty	ninety	one hundred

Table A:

City	Temperature
Portland	45
Los Angeles	
Chicago	36
Dallas	
New York	50
Miami	

Table B:

City	Temperature
Portland	
Los Angeles	79
Chicago	
Dallas	81
New York	
Miami	94

20

How old are you?

I'm 34 years old.

What's your address?

67 Main Street.

What's the temperature in New York?

It's 47 degrees.

What do you do every day?

I clean the house and I cook.

What are you doing right now?

I'm feeding the baby.

What's the weather?

It's raining.

Sunday	SUN
Monday	MON
Tuesday	TUE
Wednesday	WED
Thursday	THU
Friday	FRI
Saturday	SAT

January	JAN
February	FEB
March	MAR
April	APR
May	MAY
June	JUN
July	JUL
August	AUG
September	SEP
October	OCT
November	NOV
December	DEC

For *Foundations* Teacher's Guide
Page 57, Activity 1
Page 58, Activity 2
Page 72, Activity 2

23

©2007 Pearson Education, Inc.
Duplication for classroom use is permitted.

1533	fifteen thirty-three
102	one oh two
2099	twenty ninety-nine
1730	seventeen thirty
4401	forty-four oh one

111	one eleven
606	six oh six
728	seven twenty-eight
515	five fifteen
7053	seventy fifty-three

6 + 7	13
15 + 15	30
9 + 5	14
10 + 30	40
8 + 7	15
42 + 8	50
9 + 7	16
54 + 6	60
13 + 4	17
50 + 20	70
14 + 4	18
72 + 8	80
14 + 5	19
83 + 7	90

<table>
<tr><td></td><td></td><td></td></tr>
<tr><td></td><td></td><td></td></tr>
<tr><td></td><td></td><td></td></tr>
</table>

1. What time do you get up?

   _____

2. What time do you have breakfast?

   _____

3. What time do you go to work?

   _____

4. What time do you have lunch?

   _____

5. What time do you come home?

   _____

6. What time do you have dinner?

   _____

7. What time do you go to bed?

   _____

8. _____

   _____

Saturday	
Friday	
Thursday	
Wednesday	
Tuesday	
Monday	
Sunday	

1st	first
2nd	second
3rd	third
4th	fourth
5th	fifth
6th	sixth
7th	seventh
8th	eighth
9th	ninth
10th	tenth

11th	eleventh
12th	twelfth
13th	thirteenth
14th	fourteenth
15th	fifteenth
16th	sixteenth
17th	seventeenth
18th	eighteenth
19th	nineteenth
20th	twentieth

20th	twentieth
30th	thirtieth
40th	fortieth
50th	fiftieth
60th	sixtieth
70th	seventieth
80th	eightieth
90th	ninetieth
100th	one hundredth

A

_____	6th floor
John Smith	5th floor
Peter Smith	4th floor
_____	3rd floor
_____	2nd floor
Linda Smith	1st floor

Who lives on the _____ floor?

B

Jane Smith	6th floor
_____	5th floor
_____	4th floor
Sam Smith	3rd floor
Kim Smith	2nd floor
_____	1st floor

Who lives on the _____ floor?

33

January	1
February	2
March	3
April	4
May	5
June	6

July	**7**
August	**8**
September	**9**
October	**10**
November	**11**
December	**12**

June 12, 2008	6/12/08
January 7, 2009	1/7/09
May 11, 2007	5/11/07
November 5, 2012	11/5/12
April 10, 2011	4/10/11
October 4, 2012	10/4/12
March 9, 2011	3/9/11
September 3, 2007	9/3/07
February 8, 2010	2/8/10
July 1, 2009	7/1/09
December 6, 2008	12/6/08
August 2, 2010	8/2/10

a penny	a nickel	a dime
a quarter	a half dollar	a dollar bill
a five-dollar bill	a ten-dollar bill	a twenty-dollar bill

two quarters and a dime	60¢
three quarters and a nickel	80¢
two dimes and three pennies	23¢
four quarters	$1.00
four dimes and three nickels	55¢
eight quarters	$2.00
seven nickels and seven pennies	42¢
three nickels and twelve pennies	27¢
three quarters, two dimes, and a nickel	$1.00
three dimes and eleven pennies	41¢
three quarters and two dimes	95¢
one dime, one nickel, and one penny	16¢

How much is twelve plus two?	It's fourteen.
How much is nine plus seven?	It's sixteen.
What time is it?	It's one o'clock.
Can you come in on Tuesday at 10:15?	On Tuesday at 10:15? Yes, I can.
Can you come in on Thursday at 2:15?	On Thursday at 2:15? Yes, I can.
What floor do you live on?	I live on the fourth floor.
What's the tenth month of the year?	October.
What's the sixth month of the year?	June.
When is your birthday?	My birthday is September 21st.
What's today's date?	It's April 5, 2007.
What time does the train leave for New York?	It leaves at 6:45.

living room	kitchen	bedroom
bathroom	dining room	balcony
patio		

refrigerator	shower	closet
fireplace	stove	window

1. Is there a closet in your living room? _____

2. Is there a fireplace in your living room? _____

3. Is there a closet in your dining room? _____

4. Is there a refrigerator in your kitchen? _____

5. Is there a stove in your kitchen? _____

6. Is there a window in your kitchen? _____

7. Is there a window in your bathroom? _____

8. Is there a shower in your bathroom? _____

9. Is there a fireplace in your bedroom? _____

10. Is there a closet in your bedroom? _____

table	sofa	bed
chair	rug	lamp

The living room	a sofa a rug a lamp a TV
The kitchen	a stove a refrigerator cabinets a table
The dining room	chairs a big table a rug a lamp
Types of housing	apartment building dormitory mobile home house
Furniture	table sofa bed chair
The bathroom	bathtub shower

laundromat	bank	clinic
bakery	library	gas station
bus station	drug store	grocery store

45

post office	supermarket	hospital
park	restaurant	shopping mall
movie theater	train station	department store

A. Listen to your partner and complete the map.

_____	supermarket	_____
Main Street		
movie theater	_____	department store

B. Read these sentences to your partner. Help your partner complete the map.

1. The post office is across from the movie theater.
2. The post office is next to the supermarket.
3. The train station is across from the supermarket.
4. The train station is between the movie theater and the department store.
5. The hospital is across from the department store.
6. The hospital is next to the supermarket.

A. Listen to your partner and complete the map.

laundromat	_____	clinic
Central Street		
_____	drug store	_____

- -

B. Read these sentences to your partner. Help your partner complete the map.

1. The bus station is across from the laundromat.
2. The bus station is next to the drug store.
3. The bank is across from the drug store.
4. The bank is between the laundromat and the clinic.
5. The grocery store is across from the clinic.
6. The grocery store is next to the drug store.

Table A

Place	Location
bakery	
bank	22nd Street
bus station	
clinic	34th Street
department store	
drug store	66th Street
gas station	
grocery store	18th Street
hospital	
laundromat	90th Street
post office	
supermarket	53rd Street

Table B

Place	Location
bakery	1st Street
bank	
bus station	13th Street
clinic	
department store	85th Street
drug store	
gas station	73rd Street
grocery store	
hospital	49th Street
laundromat	
post office	11th Street
supermarket	

Where do you buy gas?	**At the gas station on Main Street.**
Where do you buy bread?	**At the bakery on Main Street.**
Where do you buy medicine?	**At the drug store on Main Street.**
Where do you buy food?	**At the supermarket on Main Street.**
Where do you buy stamps?	**At the post office on Main Street.**
Where do you wash your clothes?	**At the laundromat on Main Street.**
Where do you get your books?	**At the library on Main Street.**
Where do you eat dinner?	**At the restaurant on Main Street.**
Is there a bank nearby?	**Yes. There's a bank on Main Street.**
Where are you going?	**I'm going to the bus station on Main Street.**
Where's the hospital?	**It's on Main Street.**

young	middle-aged	old
tall	average height	short

For *Foundations* Teacher's Guide
Page 112, Activity 2
Page 116, Activity 5
Page 122, Activity 1

51

©2007 Pearson Education, Inc.
Duplication for classroom use is permitted.

brown hair	black hair	blond hair
red hair	white hair	gray hair
brown eyes	blue eyes	green eyes

single	married	divorced
widowed		

Table A:

Name	Age	Height	Hair Color	Eye Color	Marital Status
Ms. Rivera		short		brown	
Mr. Taylor	old		brown		widowed
Mrs. Johnson		average height		green	

What's his/her age?
What's his/her height?

What color hair does he/she have?
What color eyes does he/she have?
What is his/her marital status?

- -

Table B:

Name	Age	Height	Hair Color	Eye Color	Marital Status
Ms. Rivera	young		black	blue	single
Mr. Taylor		tall			
Mrs. Johnson	middle-aged		red		married

What's his/her age?
What's his/her height?

What color hair does he/she have?
What color eyes does he/she have?
What is his/her marital status?

hungry	thirsty	happy
sad	tired	angry
sick	afraid	

You're from Mexico? **What language do you speak?**	**I speak Spanish.**
You're from Korea? **What language do you speak?**	**I speak Korean.**
You're from Russia? **What language do you speak?**	**I speak Russian.**
You're from Haiti? **What language do you speak?**	**I speak Haitian.**
You're from Japan? **What language do you speak?**	**I speak Japanese.**
You're from Brazil? **What language do you speak?**	**I speak Portuguese.**
You're from Egypt? **What language do you speak?**	**I speak Arabic.**
You're from China? **What language do you speak?**	**I speak Chinese.**
You're from Greece? **What language do you speak?**	**I speak Greek.**
You're from Vietnam? **What language do you speak?**	**I speak Vietnamese.**

thin	average weight	heavy

Ms. Roberts weighs 75 pounds.	She's thin.
Mr. Kim weighs 200 pounds.	He's heavy.
Mrs. Morris weighs 125 pounds.	She's average weight.
Mr. Jones weighs 135 pounds.	He's average weight.
Jane is 10 years old.	She's young.
Mr. Smith is 45 years old.	He's middle-aged.
Mrs. Bank is 95 years old.	She's old.
Mrs. Lopez is 4 feet 10 inches tall.	She's short.
Mr. Lopez is 5 feet 8 inches tall.	He's average height.
Ms. Jackson is 6 feet 3 inches tall.	She's tall.

What's her age?	She's young.
How old are you?	I'm 26 years old.
What's his height?	He's tall.
How tall are you?	I'm five foot six.
What color hair does she have?	She has red hair.
What color hair does he have?	He has white hair.
What color eyes does she have?	She has brown eyes.
What color eyes does he have?	He has blue eyes.
What's your marital status?	I'm married.
Are you hungry?	Yes. I'm very hungry.
Are you angry?	Yes. I'm very angry.
Where are you from?	I'm from Vietnam.
What language do you speak?	I speak Portuguese.

1. What's his/her age?

2. What's his/her height?

3. What color hair does he/she have?

4. What color eyes does he/she have?

5. What's his/her weight?

6. What's his/her marital status?

7. How does he/she feel?

8. What's he/she doing?

a cookie	a banana	a carrot
a tomato	a potato	a peach
an apple	an orange	an egg
an onion		

bread	cheese	milk
cereal	butter	sugar
lettuce	soup	soda
ice cream		

Table A

Aisle 1	Aisle 2	Aisle 3	Aisle 4
cheese	cookies	soda	potatoes
milk	bread		onions
butter	sugar		carrots
			lettuce
			apples
			peaches
			oranges

You're looking for:

cereal   ice cream   soup   tomatoes   eggs

Table B

Aisle 1	Aisle 2	Aisle 3	Aisle 4
eggs	cereal	soup	potatoes
milk	sugar		onions
butter			carrots
ice cream			lettuce
			tomatoes
			apples
			oranges

You're looking for:

cheese   soda   cookies   peaches   bread

a box of	a bag of	a can of
a loaf of	a bunch of	a bottle of
a pound of	a jar of	a quart of
a dozen		

hamburger	hot dog	sandwich
cheeseburger	taco	pizza
donut	lemonade	coffee
tea		

quart	quarts	pound
pounds	half a pound	dozen
half a dozen	qt.	qts.
lb.	lbs.	1/2 lb.
doz.	1/2 doz.	

We need three pounds of cheese and a quart of milk.	**Shopping List** 3 lbs. cheese 1 qt. milk
We need a pound of cheese and two quarts of milk.	**Shopping List** 1 lb. cheese 2 qts. milk
We need a dozen eggs and a pound of apples.	**Shopping List** 1 doz. eggs 1 lb. apples
We need half a dozen eggs and two pounds of apples.	**Shopping List** 1/2 doz. eggs 2 lbs. apples
We need half a pound of tomatoes and a dozen oranges.	**Shopping List** 1/2 lb. tomatoes 1 doz. oranges
We need a pound of tomatoes and half a dozen oranges.	**Shopping List** 1 lb. tomatoes 1/2 doz. oranges
We need three quarts of milk and half a pound of onions.	**Shopping List** 3 qts. milk 1/2 lb. onions
We need a quart of milk and half a dozen of onions.	**Shopping List** 1 qt. milk 1/2 doz. onions
We need a quart of lemonade and half a pound of tomatoes.	**Shopping List** 1 qt. lemonade 1/2 lb. tomatoes
We need two quarts of lemonade and half a dozen tomatoes.	**Shopping List** 2 qts. lemonade 1/2 doz. tomatoes

are - looking - what - you - for - ?

aren't - there - any - cookies - more

any - there - sugar - isn't - more

apples - are - any - there - ?

is - any - there - cereal - ?

the - do - need - what - we - at - supermarket - ?

a - soda - we - bottle - of - need

and - loaf - we - need - bread - a
of - of - a - soup - can

like - I'd - coffee - please

help - can - I - you - ?

get - half - cheese - a - please - pound - of

What are you looking for?	A banana.
What are you looking for?	Ice cream.
Is there any milk?	No, there isn't.
Are there any peaches?	No, there aren't.
Is there any butter?	No, there isn't.
Are there any oranges?	No, there aren't.
Excuse me. I'm looking for apples.	They're in Aisle 2.
Excuse me. I'm looking for cheese.	It's in Aisle 4.
What do we need at the supermarket?	We need a box of cookies.
Can I help you?	Yes. I'd like a hot dog, please.

a shirt	a coat	a suit
a belt	a jacket	a tie
a sweater	an umbrella	a blouse
a dress	a watch	a necklace

a pair of shoes	a pair of pants	a pair of socks
a pair of jeans	a pair of gloves	a pair of mittens
a pair of pajamas		

71

1. _____ is wearing black pants.

2. _____ is wearing a brown belt.

3. _____ is wearing white shoes.

4. _____ is wearing a blue skirt.

5. _____ is wearing a yellow shirt.

6. _____ is wearing a gray blouse.

7. _____ is wearing a tie.

8. _____ is wearing a necklace.

9. _____ is wearing a green sweater.

10. _____ is wearing white socks.

Clothing	Size
shirt/blouse	
sweater	
jacket	

Clothing	Size
pants	
belt	
shoes	

Size Information (*in inches*)

Men's Shirt Sizes				
Size	S	M	L	XL
Neck	14–14½	15–15½	16–16½	17–17½
Sleeve	32–33	33–34	34–35	35–36

Women's Shirt and Dress Sizes						
Size		S		M		L
	6	8	10	12	14	16
Bust	34½	35½	36½	38	39½	41
Waist	26½	27½	28½	30	31½	33
Sleeve	30	30½	31	31½	32	32½
Hips	36½	37½	38½	40	41½	43

Men's Pants				
Size	S	M	L	XL
Waist	28–30	32–34	36–38	40–42
Inseam	30	32	33	34

Women's Pants					
Size	XS	S	M	L	XL
	0	0–2	4–6	8–10	12–14
Waist	23–24	25–26	27–28	30–32	33–35
Inseam	29	30	32	33	34

"What size _____ do you wear?"

1. _____ wears size 15 shirts.

2. _____ wears size 7 shoes.

3. _____ wears size 11 shoes.

4. _____ wears size medium sweaters.

5. _____ wears size large gloves.

6. _____ wears size large pajamas.

7. _____ wears size 36 pants.

8. _____ wears size small jackets.

9. _____ wears size 36 belts.

10. _____ wears size 12 dresses.

$10.50	ten fifty
$10.15	ten fifteen
$10.00	ten dollars
$14.00	fourteen dollars
$40.00	forty dollars
$99.00	ninety-nine dollars
$99.99	ninety-nine ninety-nine
$19.00	nineteen dollars
$60.99	sixty ninety-nine
$16.00	sixteen dollars

Table A

Clothing	Price
shirts	
belts	$24.59
gloves	
pajamas	$10.00
socks	
jeans	$46.00
shoes	
coats	$89.99

- -

Table B

Clothing	Price
shirts	$16.99
belts	
gloves	$18.50
pajamas	
socks	$2.50
jeans	
shoes	$37.00
coats	

76

May I help you?	Yes. I'm looking for a pair of mittens.
What's your favorite color?	Green.
What are you wearing today?	I'm wearing a red shirt, a black belt, and black pants.
What size do you wear?	Medium.
What's the matter with the dress?	It's too big.
What's the matter with the pants?	They're too short.
What's the price of the belts?	$10.00.
Where are the umbrellas?	Umbrellas are on the 2nd floor.
Where are women's suits?	Women's suits are on the 3rd floor.

checkbook	check	bank book
ATM card	credit card	deposit slip
withdrawal slip		

Put your ATM card into the machine.

Press in your Personal Identification Number (PIN).

Press "Withdraw Cash."

Press "Checking Account."

Press in the amount of money you want.

Take the money from the machine.

Count your money.

Take the receipt and your ATM card from the machine.

A. What are you doing?
B. I'm writing a check to Northwest Electric.
A. For how much?
B. $50.72.

A. What are you doing?
B. I'm writing a check to Dr. Jones.
A. For how much?
B. $150.00.

A. What are you doing?
B. I'm writing a check to City Hospital.
A. For how much?
B. $25.00.

A. What are you doing?
B. I'm writing a check to World Credit Cards.
A. For how much?
B. $88.24.

June 15, 2009

Pay to the order of ___Northwest Electric___ $ __50.72__

Fifty and 72/100 _____ dollars

___Vicki Chen___

June 15, 2009

Pay to the order of ___Dr. Jones___ $ __150.00__

One hundred and fifty 00/100 _____ dollars

___Vicki Chen___

June 15, 2009

Pay to the order of ___City Hospital___ $ __25.00__

Twenty-five and 00/100 _____ dollars

___Vicki Chen___

June 15, 2009

Pay to the order of ___World Credit Cards___ $ __88.24__

Eighty-eight and 24/100 _____ dollars

___Vicki Chen___

Pay to the order of _____ $ _____

_____ dollars

_____

Pay to the order of _____ $ _____

_____ dollars

_____

Pay to the order of _____ $ _____

_____ dollars

_____

Pay to the order of _____ $ _____

_____ dollars

_____

stamps	package	registered letter
money order	air letter	

Write a letter.

Put the letter in an envelope.

Write the mailing address and the return address on the envelope.

Go to the post office.

Buy a stamp for the letter.

Put the stamp on the envelope.

Put the letter in the mailbox.

Envelope A

Jim Lee

_____

_____

_____

114 Tenth Street
Dallas, Texas 75359

What's the return address?
Who is the letter going to?
How do you spell _____?

Envelope B

_____

99 Central Avenue
Chicago, Illinois 60649

Lin Wang

_____

_____

Who is the letter from?
How do you spell _____?
What's the mailing address?

That's . . .	Here's . . .	Your change is . . .
$ 6.00	$10.00	
	$20.00	$5.00
$9.50		$.50
$3.50	$5.00	
	$40.00	$8.00
$47.75		$2.25

A. That's $19.00.
B. _____
A. Your change is $1.00.

Here's $20.00.

A. That's $3.00.
B. _____
A. Your change is $2.00.

Here's $5.00.

A. That's $7.00.
B. _____
A. Your change is $3.00.

Here's $10.00.

A. That's $11.00.
B. _____
A. Your change is $4.00.

Here's $15.00.

A. That's $35.00.
B. _____
A. Your change is $5.00.

Here's $40.00.

A. That's $44.00.
B. _____
A. Your change is $6.00.

Here's $50.00.

A. That's $63.00.
B. _____
A. Your change is $7.00.

Here's $70.00.

A. That's $82.00.
B. _____
A. Your change is $8.00.

Here's $90.00.

bank	book
ATM	card
credit	card
deposit	slip
withdrawal	slip
post	office
air	letter
money	order
registered	letter
return	address
mailing	address

head	eye	ear
nose	neck	back
stomach	arm	hand
finger	leg	foot

a headache	a stomachache	a backache
an earache	a toothache	a sore throat
a cold	a cough	a fever

cough syrup	aspirin	ear drops
cold medicine	antacid tablets	throat lozenges

90

I have a cold.	You should use cold medicine.
I have a cough.	You should use cough syrup.
I have a headache.	You should use aspirin.
I have an earache.	You should use ear drops.
I have a sore throat.	You should use throat lozenges.
I have a stomachache.	You should use antacid tablets.
I have a backache.	You should use aspirin.

Compare the same medicine and the same quantity.

Medicine	Generic	Brand Name
cold medicine		
cough syrup		
aspirin		
ear drops		
antacid tablets		
throat lozenges		

Model Questions:
How much is generic *aspirin*?
How much is *Bayer® aspirin*?

I broke my arm.	I broke my leg.	I sprained my wrist.
I cut my finger.	I cut my face.	I burned my hand.

the - problem - what's - ?

you - in - come - can - 4:30 - at - tomorrow - ?

an - want - make - to - I - appointment - .

hurt - my - I - neck - .

to - sorry - I'm - that - hear - .

recommend - do - what - you - a backache - for - ?

sprained - I - my - wrist - .

recommend - Medex - cough - syrup - I - .

cut - finger - I - my - .

have - bad - a - I - backache - .

burned - I - my - foot - .

A. Emergency Operator.

B. My husband just fell and hurt his leg very badly. He can't move. Please send an ambulance.

A. What's your address?

B. 55 North Central Road.

A. And your telephone number?

B. 555–777–1234.

A. Okay. An ambulance is on the way.

1. _____ eats two meals a day.

2. _____ eats three meals a day.

3. _____ drinks six glasses of water a day.

4. _____ drinks three glasses of water a day.

5. _____ exercises three times a week.

6. _____ exercises two times a week.

7. _____ sleeps six hours a night.

8. _____ sleeps eight hours a night.

9. _____ takes a vitamin every day.

10. _____ goes to the doctor every year for a checkup.

Questions to ask your classmates:

How many meals a day do you eat?
How many glasses of water do you drink each day?
How many times a week do you exercise?
How many hours do you sleep at night?
Do you take a vitamin every day?
Do you go to the doctor every year for a checkup?

pill	tablet	capsule
caplet	teaspoon	tablespoon

Take one tablet three times a day.	1 tablet 3X/day
Take one caplet three times a day.	1 caplet 3X/day
Take two tablespoons twice a day.	2 tablespoons 2X/day
Take two teaspoons twice a day.	2 teaspoons 2X/day
Take one capsule twice a day.	1 capsule 2X/day
Take two capsules once a day.	2 capsules 1X/day
Take one teaspoon after each meal.	1 teaspoon after meals
Take one teaspoon before each meal.	1 teaspoon before meals
Take one tablet four times a day.	1 tablet 4X/day
Take four tablets once a day.	4 tablets 1X/day

Parts of the Body: Head	face eye nose ear
Parts of the Body: Arm	hand wrist finger
Ailments	cough fever toothache sore throat
Injuries	I broke my arm. I sprained my wrist. I burned my face. I hurt my foot.
Drug Store Medicines	aspirin cold medicine ear drops vitamins
Forms of Medicines	capsule tablet caplet pill

What's the matter?	I have an earache.
What happened?	I broke my leg.
I have a stomachache. What should I do?	You should use antacid tablets.
I have a headache. What should I do?	You should use aspirin.
Where can I find eardrops?	Look in Aisle 4.
Can you come in tomorrow at 2:15?	Yes, that's fine.
What's your address?	4561 Broadway.
What's your telephone number?	908–444–1992.
How many times a week do you exercise?	Twice a week.
How many meals do you eat a day?	Three a day.
What do you recommend for a sore throat?	I recommend Comex throat lozenges.

English teacher	principal	school nurse
P.E. teacher	guidance counselor	custodian
school librarian		

math	English	social studies
science	art	music
technology		

band	orchestra	choir
drama	football	soccer
basketball		

Schedule A

Period	Class	Room
1st		345
2nd	Math	
3rd		418
4th	Lunch	
5th		310
6th	Social Studies	
7th		113
8th	Science	

What class do we have _____ period?

In which classroom do we have _____?

Schedule B

Period	Class	Room
1st	English	
2nd		215
3rd	Art	
4th		cafeteria
5th	Technology	
6th		201
7th	Music	
8th		214

What class do we have _____ period?

In which classroom do we have _____?

School Match Game | 105

Who's that?	That's the English teacher.
Where are you going?	To the cafeteria.
What's your favorite subject?	Social studies.
What are you going to do after school today?	I have soccer practice.
What class do you have third period?	I have music.
I'm going to the nurse's office because . . .	I have a headache.
I have P.E. class in . . .	the gym.
I have drama practice in . . .	the auditorium.
I have lunch in . . .	the cafeteria.
The librarian works in . . .	the library.
The person who cleans the school is . . .	the custodian.

a cook	a custodian	a gardener
a cashier	an electrician	a repairperson
a delivery person	a security guard	a police officer
a construction worker		

a bus driver	a painter	a teacher
a baker	a secretary	a taxi driver
a truck driver	a plumber	a mechanic
a carpenter		

For *Foundations* Teacher's Guide
Page 222, Activity 1
Page 223, Activity 10

107

©2007 Pearson Education, Inc.
Duplication for classroom use is permitted.

drive a bus	paint	teach
bake	type	drive a taxi
drive a truck	fix sinks	fix cars
repair buildings		

a waitress	a waiter	a housekeeper
an assembler	a doctor	a salesperson
a pharmacist		

1. _____ works in a hospital.

2. _____ works in a store.

3. _____ works at home.

4. _____ works in a hotel.

5. _____ works in a restaurant.

6. _____ can drive a car.

7. _____ can bake and cook.

8. _____ can type.

9. _____ can paint.

10. _____ can fix cars.

<u>Questions to ask your classmates:</u>

Where do you work?

Can you _____?

assemble components	cook	sell clothing
cut hair	repair watches	operate equipment
use a cash register		

A baker . . .	bakes.
A bus driver . . .	drives a bus.
A cashier . . .	uses a cash register.
A secretary . . .	can type.
A carpenter . . .	can repair buildings.
A mechanic . . .	can fix cars.
An assembler . . .	can assemble things.
A plumber . . .	can fix sinks.
A repairperson . . .	can repair things.
A barber . . .	cuts hair.
A salesperson . . .	sells things in a store.

supply room	cafeteria	mailroom
bathroom	employee lounge	personnel office
vending machine		

wet - the - is - floor - .

your - on - safety - put - glasses - .

there - don't - stand - !

telling - me - for - thanks - .

that - go - don't - room - in - !

in - smoke - don't - here - .

a - wear - helmet - .

What do you do?	I'm a delivery person.
What kind of job are you looking for?	I'm looking for a job as a security guard.
Can you type?	Yes, I can. I'm an experienced secretary.
Can you repair buildings?	Yes, I can. I'm an experienced carpenter.
Can you fix cars?	Yes, I can. I'm an experienced mechanic.
Can you fix sinks?	Yes, I can. I'm an experienced plumber.
Tell me about your job skills. What can you do?	I can paint. I can fix sinks. I can drive a truck.
Where do you work?	At the Midtown Hotel.
Can you operate equipment?	No, I can't operate equipment. But I'm sure I can learn quickly.
What's the matter?	I'm sick.
Where's the cafeteria?	Down the hall.

cut	hair
sell	clothing
repair	watches
fix	sinks
drive	a taxi
use	a cash register
operate	equipment
assemble	components
drive	a bus
type	letters
fix	cars

A. Listen to your partner and complete the map.

bank		_____
_____		post office
park		_____
train station		_____

B. Read these sentences to your partner. Help your partner complete the map.

1. The laundromat is on the right.
2. The laundromat is across from the train station.
3. The movie theater is on the right.
4. The movie theater is across from the bank.
5. The hospital is on the left.
6. The hospital is across from the post office.
7. The hospital is between the park and the bank.
8. The library is on the right.
9. The library is across from the park.
10. The library is between the laundromat and the post office.

A. Listen to your partner and complete the map.

_____		library
bus station		_____
_____		movie theater
park		_____

- -

B. Read these sentences to your partner. Help your partner complete the map.
1. The post office is on the right.
2. The post office is between the library and the movie theater.
3. The clinic is on the left.
4. The clinic is across from the library.
5. The laundromat is across from the park.
6. The laundromat is next to the movie theater.
7. The bank is on the left.
8. The bank is between the bus station and the park.

How do you get to work?

	Number of People
walk	
take a bus	
take a subway	
take a taxi	
drive a car	
ride a bicycle	

1. Do you like to walk? Why?/Why not?

   _____

2. Do you walk every day?

   _____

3. Where do you walk?

   _____

4. Do you like to take the bus? Why?/Why not?

   _____

5. Do you take the bus every day?

   _____

6. Where do go on the bus?

   _____

7. Do you like to drive? Why?/Why not?

   _____

8. Do you drive every day?

   _____

9. Where do you drive?

   _____

10. Do you like to ride a bicycle? Why?/Why not?

    _____

11. Do you ride your bicycle every day?

    _____

12. Where do ride your bicycle?

    _____

1. The first bus leaves Center Street at _____.

2. It's 4:20. The next bus arrives at School Street at _____.

3. It's 6:45 in the morning. The next bus arrives at School Street at _____.

4. It's 7:45 at night. The next bus arrives at River Road at _____.

5. It's 10:15 in the morning. The next bus arrives at Lee Avenue at _____.

6. It's 12:35 PM. The next bus arrives at Wilson Avenue at _____.

7. It's 3:55. The next bus to leave Center Street is at _____.

8. The first bus arrives at River Road at _____.

do - get - how - to - the - I - post office - ?

bank - the - right - the - is - on - .

way - that - walk - .

the library - is - the hospital - and - between - the park - .

the - the - is - next - to - bus station - laundromat - .

the - do - need - what - we - at - supermarket - ?

do - where - get - I - off - for - Dacy's Department store - ?

how - you - to - do - get - school - ?

sign - speed - limit - says - the - 25 - .

driving - too - fast - you're - !

go - you - can't - on - that - street - !

play soccer	play basketball	play tennis
watch TV	listen to music	exercise
go jogging	go swimming	go rollerblading
go dancing		

1. _____ likes to play soccer.

2. _____ likes to play basketball.

3. _____ likes to play tennis.

4. _____ likes to watch TV.

5. _____ likes to listen to music.

6. _____ likes to exercise.

7. _____ likes to go jogging.

8. _____ likes to go swimming.

9. _____ likes to go rollerblading.

10. _____ likes to go dancing.

Question to ask your classmates:

Do you like to _____?

1. Do you like to watch TV? _____

2. Do you watch TV every day? _____

3. Where do you watch TV? _____

4. How much time do you watch TV every week? _____

5. Do you like to exercise? _____

6. Do you exercise every day? _____

7. Where do you exercise? _____

8. How much time do you exercise every week? _____

9. Do you like to listen to music? _____

10. Do you listen to music every day? _____

11. Where do you listen to music? _____

12. Do you like to go dancing? _____

13. Where do you go dancing? _____

go jogging	see a movie	go to the park
see a play	go to a concert	play baseball
play golf	go to a ballgame	go to a museum
go to the zoo		

1. _____ is going to see a movie.

2. _____ is going to go to the park.

3. _____ is going to see a play.

4. _____ is going to go to a concert.

5. _____ is going to play baseball.

6. _____ is going to play golf.

7. _____ is going to go jogging.

8. _____ is going to go to a ballgame.

9. _____ is going to go to a museum.

10. _____ is going to go to the zoo.

<u>Question to ask your classmates:</u>

Are you going to _____ next weekend?

played soccer	played basketball	played tennis
watched TV	listened to music	exercised
went jogging	went swimming	went rollerblading
went dancing		

128

saw a movie	went to the park	saw a play
went to a concert	played baseball	played golf
went to a ballgame	went to a museum	went to the zoo

Activity	Number of Students

SUN	MON	TUE	WED	THU	FRI	SAT

What are you going to do on _____ ?

Calendar A:

JUNE

SUN	MON	TUE	WED	THU	FRI	SAT
1 have lunch with Jim	**2** work	**3** go jogging work	**4** work have dinner with Jane	**5** go jogging work	**6** work	**7** go to the zoo
8 go to a ballgame	**9** work	**10** go jogging work	**11** work	**12** go jogging work	**13** work see a play	**14** go dancing

Calendar B:

JUNE

SUN	MON	TUE	WED	THU	FRI	SAT
1 ____	**2** work	**3** ____ work	**4** work ____	**5** go jogging work	**6** work	**7** ____
8 go to a ballgame	**9** work	**10** go jogging work	**11** work	**12** ____ work	**13** ____ ____	**14** ____

What are you going to do on _____?

Calendar A:

JUNE

SUN	MON	TUE	WED	THU	FRI	SAT
15 work	**16** work	**17** work	**18** exercise go to a movie	**19** go to a museum	**20** work play basketball	**21** work
22 go to the zoo	**23** work	**24** work	**25** exercise have lunch with Kate	**26** clean the house	**27** work play basketball	**28** work

Calendar B:

JUNE

SUN	MON	TUE	WED	THU	FRI	SAT
15 work	**16** work	**17** ___	**18** exercise	**19** ___	**20** work ___	**21** work
22 ___	**23** work	**24** work	**25** exercise ___	**26** ___	**27** work play basketball	**28** ___